It's another Quality Book from CGP

This book is for anyone studying OCR GCSE Resistant Materials.

It explains all the technical details you'll need to understand, with plenty of full-colour diagrams to help make everything crystal-clear.

We've also included advice to help make your project a winner, plus tips on how to improve your exam techniques.

What CGP is all about

Our sole aim here at CGP is to produce the highest quality books — carefully written, immaculately presented and dangerously close to being funny.

Then we work our socks off to get them out to you — at the cheapest possible prices.

Contents

SECTION ONE — THE DESIGN PROCESS

SECTION TWO — MATERIALS AND COMPONENTS

SECTION THREE — TOOLS AND PROCESSES

SECTION FOUR — MARKET INFLUENCES

SECTION FIVE — INDUSTRIAL AWARENESS

Published by CGP

Editors:
Katie Braid, Katherine Craig, Ben Fletcher, Rosie Gillham, Sarah Hilton, Adam Moorhouse,
Ali Palin, Hayley Thompson.

Contributors:
Catherine Atsiaris, Ryan Ball, Debbie McGrory, John Nichols.

With thanks to Paul Anderson for the content review.
With thanks to Simon Little and Adrian Lee for the proofreading.

With thanks to Laura Stoney for the copyright research.

ISBN: 978 1 84762 352 2

With thanks to BSI for permission to reproduce the Kitemark symbol on page 56. Kitemark and the
Kitemark symbol are registered trademarks of BSI. For more information visit www.kitemark.com.

With thanks to the Forest Stewardship Council for permission to reproduce the logo on page 56,
© 1996 Forest Stewardship Council A.C.

Page 76 contains public sector information published by the Health and Safety Executive and licensed
under the Open Government Licence v3.0.

Photographs of original oak furniture by Neil Connor on page 21 and 37 reproduced by kind permission
of Anja Connor.

Every effort has been made to locate copyright holders and obtain permission to reproduce sources.
For those sources where it has been difficult to trace the originator of the work, we would be grateful for
information. If any copyright holder would like us to make an amendment to the acknowledgements,
please notify us and we will gladly update the book at the next reprint. Thank you.

Clipart from Corel®

Printed by Elanders Ltd, Newcastle upon Tyne.

Based on the classic CGP style created by Richard Parsons.

Project Advice

Unlike most subjects, in D&T you actually get to <u>make something useful</u> (well, hopefully).

The <u>Projects</u> are Worth 60% of your GCSE

1) Your D&T <u>projects</u> are called '<u>controlled assessments</u>'.

2) There are two projects — for the first one you have to <u>produce and evaluate a prototype</u>, and for the second one you have to <u>design and manufacture</u> a product.

3) Your teacher will give you as much help as they're allowed to by the exam board, so do <u>ask them</u>... but mostly it's <u>up to you</u> to make a <u>good job</u> of your projects.

4) You can dip into this book for a bit of extra help. Section 1 is all about the design process, so if you're not sure <u>where to start</u>, that might be a good place to look.

5) If you're wondering about a particular <u>detail</u> — what type of <u>hinge</u> to use, say — it's probably quickest to look that up in the <u>index</u> and go straight to those pages.

Only Put <u>Relevant Stuff</u> in your Folders

Your teacher will give you plenty of guidance on what needs to go in your folders, but here are some <u>tips</u>:

1) You should include lots of <u>info</u> and <u>detail</u>... but your work needs to be <u>concise</u> and <u>to the point</u>.

2) So <u>DON'T</u> waste space on <u>irrelevant</u> stuff, especially at the <u>research</u> stage. For example:

> Suppose you've analysed some existing <u>TV cupboards</u>, looking at how the doors were attached... Don't <u>bore the examiners stupid</u> with detailed descriptions of every TV cupboard hinge within a ten mile radius of your school.
>
> A <u>brief summary</u> of your research findings is all that's needed — then the really important thing to say is how those findings <u>helped you decide</u> how to attach the doors in <u>your product</u>.

3) <u>DO</u> put in lots of <u>photos</u>. The examiners love this. They want to see photos of:

- Any <u>models</u> you make (see p. 10). Don't just put in photos of the ones that worked. In fact, the ones that <u>didn't quite work</u> are more useful because then you can explain <u>what was wrong</u> and how you fixed it.

- The <u>intermediate stages</u> of making your final product — part of the way through the assembly process, say — to show <u>how you constructed</u> it.

4) <u>CHECK</u> that you've used the right <u>technical words</u> and <u>spelled</u> things correctly. And make sure you've <u>explained things clearly</u> — get someone who <u>knows nothing</u> about your project to read it and see if it <u>makes sense</u>.

Here's me with the manufacturer's specification.

The Exam is Worth 40%

1) There's one exam, which will cover <u>everything</u> you've learned during the course — materials, tools, how to design things, how to make things, health and safety, environmental issues...

2) This book can help you <u>learn all that stuff</u> — and has <u>questions</u> for you to <u>check</u> what you know.

3) There's a <u>glossary</u> at the back of the book, in case you need to sort out your thermosetting plastics from your thermoplastics.

4) The <u>exam technique</u> section (pages 78-81) has some <u>worked examples</u> of exam-style questions, and some hints on how to make sure you get <u>top marks</u>.

Controlled Assessment — nope, it's not funny...

Most of the controlled assessment marks depend on the <u>sheer brilliance</u> of your <u>folders</u>, so don't worry if your products aren't perfect — you'll get loads of marks for being dead <u>critical</u> in your <u>evaluations</u>.

Design Issues

Designing is all about coming up with new products that people want to buy.

Good Designs Can Make People's Lives Easier

1) Well designed products can improve people's quality of life.

2) For example, a new design of car might be more comfortable, easier to drive and more economical. A well designed walking frame could help a disabled person to move around more easily.

3) The wider the choice of products available, the greater the chance that consumers will find products to benefit them.

New Products Are Designed For Different Reasons

There are several reasons why a new product might be designed. Designers have to respond to:

CHANGING STYLES AND TASTE

1) Designers design stuff (and manufacturers make it) to satisfy the wants and needs of consumers — consumer demand. Market pull is when new or improved products are designed as a result of consumer demand.

2) Changing fashions and social attitudes affect the kind of products people want — consumer demand won't always be for the same things or styles.

Bill was a consumer in dire need of a new razor.

3) For example, the car was invented to transport people from A to B, but now consumers expect it to be more of a status symbol, with luxury extras like air conditioning and seat-back TV screens.

ADVANCES IN TECHNOLOGY

1) In industry, research and development departments are always coming up with new technologies, materials and manufacturing techniques. This can drive the design of new products.

2) Manufacturers can use new technology to develop new products, or to improve existing ones.

3) Using new technology might make an existing product cheaper, better at its function or nicer-looking — all things which will make products easier to sell.

4) For example, computers started off as huge mechanical 'adding machines'. Now, thanks to improvements in technology, you can buy a sleek, portable laptop that's small but really fast and powerful.

ENVIRONMENTAL PRESSURES

1) Some new designs are developed because existing ones aren't sustainable.

2) For example, as the oil supply runs out, designers will have to find alternatives to some of the plastic products that are made from oil.

3) To reduce energy use, many designers are working out how to make products more energy efficient.

Learn these design issues, or you'll have serious exam issues...

Designers don't just come up with ideas randomly. Products are made because there's a need for them — whether it's consumer demand, changes in technology, or environmental pressures.

Design Issues

Design and Manufacture Has Become Globalised

1) Before there were good transport and communication links, most products were designed, manufactured and sold in the <u>same country</u>.

2) Now it's common for products to be designed in one country, manufactured in another, and then sold all over the world. This is known as <u>globalisation</u> (see page 73 for more).

3) Some products are made in <u>more than one</u> country. For example, a car may have components made all over the world before it's assembled in one place.

4) The globalisation of products has advantages and disadvantages:

Advantages

- Production <u>costs less</u> because <u>materials</u> can be sourced from where they're cheapest and taken for processing to countries where <u>wages</u> and <u>energy</u> are cheap.
- The savings made during production may be passed on to <u>consumers</u> as <u>lower prices</u>.
- Consumers have greater <u>product choice</u> — they can buy products from all over the world.
- Manufacturers can sell their products <u>worldwide</u>, making <u>more money</u>.

Disadvantages

- More <u>energy</u> is used and more <u>pollution</u> is created because materials, parts and finished products are transported from country to country.
- Designing can become more <u>complicated</u> — products designed to be sold worldwide need to take into account many different <u>cultures</u>, be suitable for different <u>power sources</u> and may need to have instructions in <u>different languages</u>.
- Some people think that globalisation <u>reduces</u> the <u>variety of design</u>, with products from different places and cultures becoming more and more <u>similar</u>.
- Companies may use factories <u>abroad</u> to take advantage of <u>cheap labour</u> and more relaxed <u>labour laws</u>. Products <u>designed</u> and <u>sold</u> in Britain may have been <u>made</u> in factories abroad with <u>working conditions</u> that would be <u>illegal</u> here.

Practice Questions

1) a) What is meant by <u>market pull</u>?
   b) Give one example of a product that's been introduced because of advances in <u>technology</u>.

2) Why might running out of oil make life harder for manufacturers of <u>plastic products</u>?

3) a) Why has <u>globalisation</u> made manufacturing <u>cheaper</u>?
   b) Why has <u>globalisation</u> made some designing more <u>complicated</u>?

4) Arthur is designing an MP3 player.
   How might advances in <u>technology</u> affect his design?

5) Jacob owns a UK based firm that manufactures and sells sheds in the UK only.
   Suggest ways in which <u>globalisation</u> could help Jacob.

Product Analysis and Market Research

If you design and make <u>products that people want to buy</u>, you could become a millionaire.

Designing Starts with the Design Brief

So, someone gets an idea for a <u>new product</u>.
They decide to <u>employ a designer</u> to work on the idea.

1) The person who hires the designer is called the <u>client</u>.
2) The <u>client</u> gives the designer a <u>design brief</u>...
3) The design brief is a <u>starting point</u> for the development of the product. It should include:

- what <u>kind</u> of product is needed (and <u>why</u>)
- how the product will be <u>used</u>
- <u>who</u> the product is <u>for</u> (the <u>target market</u>)

4) The designer needs to pick out all the <u>important features</u> of the design brief.
5) One way of doing this is by drawing a <u>spider diagram</u>. It's a quick way to analyse the problem and decide what you need to <u>research</u>.

DESIGN BRIEF FOR BACKSCRATCHER/TURNIP HOLDER

No currently commercially available backscratcher has an in-built capacity for turnip storage. We want you to design a product to meet this need for those people having itchy backs and modest turnip storage requirements (up to 4 turnips).

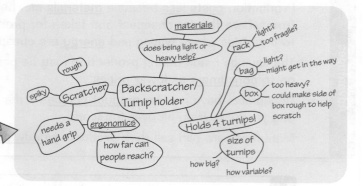

Product Analysis Can Give You Ideas for Your Design

As part of your <u>research</u> you'll need to <u>analyse existing products</u> — this can help you with your own design. There are lots of things to consider when you're analysing an existing product:

FUNCTION AND FITNESS FOR PURPOSE:
<u>Function</u> is what the product is <u>intended</u> to do. <u>Fitness for purpose</u> is <u>how well</u> the product can <u>do this function</u>. To find out whether a product is fit for purpose you need to <u>test it</u>, e.g. if it's a chair, sit on it, or if it's a toy, play with it.

MATERIALS AND MANUFACTURE: Work out <u>what materials</u> have been used and why — what <u>properties</u> they have (see pages 16-17). You should also consider the <u>processes</u> that have been used to make the product, e.g. which <u>techniques</u> were used to <u>shape</u> the various parts.

<u>Disassembling</u> (taking apart) a product can help you find out <u>how a product was made</u> and <u>how it works</u>. Make <u>careful notes</u> as you disassemble something. Record what <u>materials</u> and <u>components</u> have been used and how it's <u>structured</u> — use sketches or photos to help. And make sure you work <u>safely</u> — you don't want to disassemble your <u>fingers</u> or <u>face</u> instead.

COMPETITION AND COST: You need to consider <u>value for money</u>. For example, if you're looking at a <u>hairdryer</u>, find out whether it's cheaper or more expensive than <u>similar</u> hairdryers. You'll also need to look at <u>how it performs</u> compared to these other hairdryers.

TARGET MARKET: Try to work out what <u>group</u> of people the product is aimed at. You can often tell this from the product's <u>aesthetics</u> (appearance) and its <u>ergonomics</u> (see page 8).

Design briefs — to go with your design socks...

You probably think this seems a lot to think about before starting on the design of a product. But it's all worth doing. There's no point coming up with a <u>new product</u> if it's no better than an <u>old one</u>...

Product Analysis and Market Research

You Need to Analyse the Sustainability of Products

When you analyse products, think about the environmental impact of the materials and processes used.

1) Some materials are toxic, e.g. some paints and varnishes.

2) Many materials are made from finite resources. For example, there's only a limited amount of metal ores in the Earth's crust. Most plastics are made from crude oil, which will eventually run out.

3) It's better to use renewable materials, e.g. wood. Softwoods (which can be regrown in a person's lifetime) are a better choice than hardwoods (which take a long time to grow).

4) Products that use recycled materials are also more environmentally friendly.

5) Many products are thrown away — it's good if these products are made from recyclable materials or biodegradable materials (those that can rot away naturally). For example, waste wood is biodegradable and can also be recycled into manufactured boards (see page 19).

6) Manufacturing processes are important too. Processes that don't create much pollution or waste material are more sustainable than those that do. Processes that use a lot of energy (moulding plastics, say, because it needs high temperatures to melt the plastic) have a bigger environmental impact. See page 66.

Do Market Research to find out What Customers Want

1) The point of doing market research (questionnaires, interviews, etc.) is to:
   - find out what people like or dislike about similar existing products.
   - check that people will actually want your product.

2) Even the best products won't be everyone's cup of tea — some people will like them and some won't.

3) You need to work out which people are most likely to buy your product (the design brief should help)...

4) ...and ask them what they want the product to be like.

5) Then you need to make sure that the size and proportions will fit the user's needs — ergonomics (page 8). For example, a hand-held product needs to fit well in the hand and the buttons need to be easily reachable. You can do research to find out user's body measurement data (anthropometrics).

Practice Questions

1) a) What information does a design brief include?
   b) In industry, who writes the design brief?

2) What is fitness for purpose?

3) Katie is disassembling a coffee grinder. What useful information can she get by doing this?

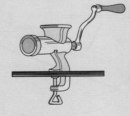

4) Gilbert is analysing this product. He finds that some of the parts are made from plastics, some are metal and some are made from wood.
   a) Who is the target market for the product?
   b) Which of the materials in the toy are made from finite resources?

5) What's the point of doing market research?

Design Specification and Proposals

Once you've got your design brief sorted and you've done some research, you should use your research findings to help you decide what your product should be like — it's design specification time.

The Design Specification is a List of Conditions to Meet

1) The design specification gives certain conditions that the product must meet. These conditions should take account of your research findings.

> E.g. if you know that people in your target market wouldn't want to buy a backscratcher that costs more than £100, your design specification might include the statement, "Must cost £100 or less."

2) It's best to write a specification as bullet points rather than a paragraph of explanations. Include points to describe some or all of the following:

1. The product's function	4. Size
2. Aesthetics — how it will look, feel, smell, sound...	5. Safety points to consider
3. Materials, equipment and production method	6. Price range

Example:
- The backscratcher/turnip holder should weigh 300 g or less.
- It should be multicoloured.
- The minimum length will be 400 mm.
- It should be easy to grip but not feel rough.

You Need to Produce a Range of Design Ideas

Once you've written your specification it's time to be creative — you have to come up with some ideas.

1) Don't just go with the first thing you think of — dream up a few quite different designs (see the next page for some ways to get inspiration). Let your imagination run wild for a bit...

2) Sketch each idea and annotate it (add notes) to explain it fully.

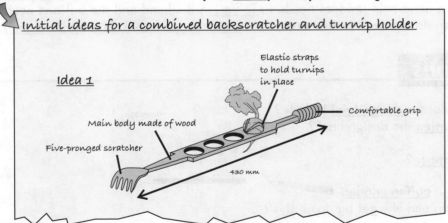

Initial ideas for a combined backscratcher and turnip holder

Idea 1

Elastic straps to hold turnips in place

Comfortable grip

Main body made of wood

Five-pronged scratcher

430 mm

EXAM TIP
Your initial ideas should be sketched freehand in pencil fairly quickly.

3) Once you've got a few possible designs, you need to check that you could actually make the designs. Creativity is a splendid thing... but total impracticality isn't.

Aesthetics, costs — this designing lark's so materialistic...

Your design specification covers all the important stuff — what your product will do, what it'll look like and be made of, and how much it'll all cost. And all of this is tied up with what materials you'll be using.

Design Specification and Proposals

Be Creative...

You could get <u>ideas</u> from lots of different places.
Nature can be a design inspiration for the <u>structure</u>, <u>function</u> or <u>aesthetics</u> (look) of a product.

Structure

The massive <u>domes</u> at the <u>Eden Project</u> are a very
strong, lightweight structure, just like a <u>honeycomb</u>.

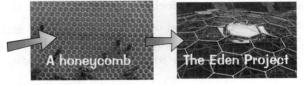

A honeycomb   The Eden Project

Function

<u>Cats' eyes</u> for <u>roads</u> were invented in the 1930s by Percy Shaw.
He was inspired by the way cats' eyes <u>reflect light in the dark</u>.

Aesthetics

A good technique is the <u>close-up effect</u>. This is where you look
at just a <u>small section</u> of an image. For example, you could
design some jewellery based on a close-up of part of a flower.

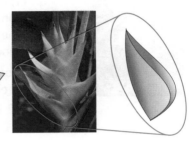

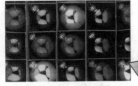

This packaging uses
repeated squares.

<u>Patterns</u> using <u>grids</u> and <u>repeating shapes</u> are often used in product
design. Many products, especially <u>packaging</u>, are based on <u>simple
geometric shapes</u> such as squares, rectangles, circles and triangles.

Use the Specification to Evaluate Your Ideas

1) Your design specification should act as a <u>guide</u> to make sure that
   the product will do what you want it to.

2) Use the specification to help <u>evaluate</u> your <u>initial ideas</u>. Ask yourself
   <u>how well</u> each idea meets each of the points in your specification.

3) You'll have to pick <u>one idea</u> to develop <u>further</u> — make sure you pick
   one that's <u>original</u>, <u>creative</u> and fits the specification really well.

4) You'll need to <u>justify</u> your choice and explain why you <u>rejected</u> the other ideas.

You'll also use the design
specification to evaluate
your final product.

Practice Questions

1) a) What is a <u>design specification</u>?
   b) List some points that the design specification for an egg cup might include.
   c) Write a design specification for a combined egg cup/toast rack.

2) Ash is trying to design a <u>basin</u> for his friend's new bathroom.
   Here is the design specification:

   • a modern look
   • no sharp edges
   • less than 50 cm long by 30 cm wide
   • must include holes for taps
   • easy to clean
   • at least 20 cm deep

   a) Suggest something in <u>nature</u> that Ash could use as an inspiration.
   b) Make an <u>annotated sketch</u> of a design inspired by your suggestion.
   c) Use whatever method you like to come up with <u>two more</u>
      initial ideas, and sketch and annotate these designs too.

Development

So, you've got a super duper brilliant idea — now you need to make sure the design is suitable for the people in your target market to use. Which leads us smoothly on to <u>ergonomics</u> and <u>anthropometrics</u>.

Ergonomics *Is About Making the Product Fit the User*

Making a product comfortable and easy to use is known as <u>ergonomics</u>.

1) Products need to be designed so that their <u>size</u> and <u>proportions</u> fit the needs of the user. For example, the buttons on a phone need to be big enough for the user to press them individually.

2) Ergonomic design also ensures that <u>using</u> the product won't cause <u>health problems</u>. For example, an ergonomically designed chair would prevent you suffering backache from using the chair regularly. Many chair designs achieve this by allowing you to have your feet on the <u>floor</u> with your knees at a <u>right angle</u> and your <u>back</u> supported.

3) Ergonomics need to take the <u>target market</u> into account, e.g. a chair for a five-year-old needs to be a different size from a chair for a fifteen-year-old (obviously).

Anthropometric Data *are* Measurements *of* Humans

To make your product the <u>right size</u>, you need to know the likely <u>body measurements</u> of the <u>users</u>. Measurements of human body parts are called <u>anthropometric data</u>.

1) First, work out <u>what measurements</u> you need. For example, if your product is a novelty mask it doesn't matter how long the users' legs are — you only need to know about their heads.

2) <u>Find out</u> what these measurements are on the <u>typical user</u> of the product.
(The best way is to sample lots of people from the target group then take the average.)

3) Design your product to fit someone with <u>these average measurements</u>.

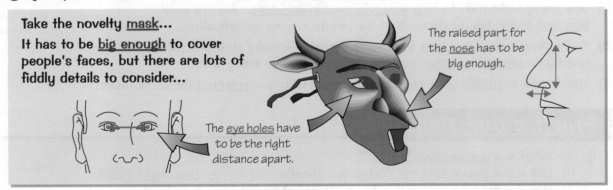

Take the novelty <u>mask</u>...
It has to be <u>big enough</u> to cover people's faces, but there are lots of fiddly details to consider...

The <u>eye holes</u> have to be the right distance apart.

The raised part for the <u>nose</u> has to be big enough.

4) BUT a product that fits <u>only</u> the <u>average</u> person <u>isn't</u> the best solution (most people <u>aren't</u> average).

5) So designers often aim to make the product fit <u>okay</u> for <u>90%</u> of the target users. For example, they'd make the nose of the mask bigger than needed for the average nose.

Make sure you're comfortable with these pages...

We'd really struggle if products weren't designed with the <u>user</u> in mind. There'd be all kinds of crazy-sized stuff out there, and aches and pains all round. Hurrah for anthropometrics and ergonomics...

Development

The point of development is to think about the <u>details</u> of your design — and try to get everything right.

Choose the Materials Carefully

Designers need to choose what <u>materials</u> to make products from. There are several factors to think about:

1) Function — you need to use materials with properties that are <u>suitable</u> for the function. For example, if you were making a bed for elephants, you'd need materials strong enough to support their weight (e.g. steel). If you want a <u>portable</u> product, you'd need materials light enough to carry around. See pages 16-17 for more on materials and their properties.

2) Aesthetics — the look of your product must appeal to the <u>target market</u>. For example, traditional oak furniture with brass fittings might appeal to older people. Younger people might prefer stuff made from brightly coloured polypropylene.

Ruby encrusted solid gold photo frame — only 50p!

3) Cost — if you're going to sell a product <u>cheaply</u> you <u>can't</u> spend loads on really expensive materials to make it.

4) Environmental and social issues — using <u>sustainable materials</u> (see below) can limit the environmental impact of the product. The use of some materials can also have a negative <u>social</u> impact. For example, activities such as logging or mining (to provide materials) may drive people off their land and destroy their livelihoods.

Keep Sustainability in Mind

Think about whether you could <u>improve</u> the sustainability of your design by:

1) Using <u>different materials</u>, e.g. cornstarch (a renewable, biodegradable resource) instead of polyethylene.
2) <u>Adding</u> a feature, e.g. adding solar panels to a clock to provide renewable energy.
3) <u>Reducing</u> the amount of <u>material</u> used, e.g. making the lead on a kettle shorter.

Practice Questions

1) a) What is meant by <u>ergonomics</u>?
   b) Suggest what needs to be considered when designing a <u>computer keyboard</u> to make it 'ergonomically' designed.
   c) What might happen to the person using the keyboard if it's <u>badly designed</u>?

2) Susanna is analysing a <u>coffee grinder</u> that's been designed using <u>anthropometric data</u>.
   a) What is anthropometric data?
   b) Suggest <u>one part</u> of the coffee grinder that anthropometric data would be needed for.
   c) <u>What</u> should Susanna check about this part?

3) Josie is designing a <u>folding table</u> to be used by <u>campers</u>.
   She is choosing materials for the <u>table top</u> and <u>legs</u>.
   a) Describe some <u>functional</u> considerations Josie should bear in mind.
   b) What <u>aesthetic</u> considerations should she bear in mind?
   c) What <u>cost</u> considerations should she bear in mind?

Modelling

There's only so much <u>development</u> you can do <u>on paper</u> — the rest is done through <u>modelling</u>...

Detailed Sketches Help You Work Out the Finer Points

1) Your <u>initial sketches</u> will probably have been <u>rough</u>, <u>freehand</u> pencil drawings.

2) Trying out some more <u>detailed drawings</u> is the next stage.

3) It helps you to see what will actually <u>work</u> in practice and it might help you decide on <u>details</u> you hadn't thought about before, e.g. the sizes or positions of components or how parts should be <u>constructed</u> and <u>fitted together</u>.

See pages 14-15 for lots of different drawing techniques.

Use Modelling to Improve Your Design

1) Modelling is just making <u>practice versions</u> of your design, or parts of your design. It's a good way to spot (and solve) <u>problems</u>.

2) Make models using materials that are <u>easy</u> and <u>quick</u> to work with, e.g. cardboard, foam board, corrugated plastic (corriflute), MDF, plasticard, STYROFOAM™...

3) You can also use the modelling stage to <u>try out</u> different <u>components</u> and <u>construction methods</u>...

4) ...and think about whether you could <u>reduce</u> the number of <u>parts</u> to make construction easier.

Not that kind of model...

You can also use <u>CAD/CAM</u> to help with the modelling process (see p. 54-55).
- You can make <u>virtual models</u> (in 3D) using <u>CAD</u>.
- You can use <u>CAD/CAM</u> to do <u>rapid prototyping</u> — you draw the design in CAD and use a <u>3D printer</u> to make the model.

Test and Evaluate Each Model

1) After you've made the first model, do some <u>tests</u> to check that it's how it should be.

2) You'll probably find there are some things that <u>don't work out</u> quite how you'd hoped:

The cabinet <u>looked great</u> but the <u>doors</u> just <u>couldn't be opened</u>.

3) <u>Write down</u> what the problem is, and suggest how to <u>fix it</u>, e.g. use a different type of hinge.

4) Record how the design develops — <u>take photos</u> of your models.

5) You should also <u>evaluate</u> each model against the <u>design specification</u>. Take each point on the specification and see if your model is up to scratch.

6) You might end up having to <u>modify</u> your <u>specification</u> after you've evaluated your models.

You can also experiment to find out how much <u>margin for error</u> there is — the <u>tolerance</u> (see page 70). For example, it might not matter if you made the <u>hands</u> on a <u>clock</u> a tiny bit too short — it'll still work and probably look fine. However, accuracy <u>would</u> matter if you made a door that was a tiny bit too big — it <u>might not shut</u>.

Modelling — take your product down the catwalk...

If you find out that something just <u>can't</u> work or is going to be <u>too expensive</u>, it's OK to change your design — as long as you explain <u>why</u> you've changed it. That's the whole point of testing and evaluation.

Modelling

Keep Going Until You Get it Just Right

You might find that you end up changing something, then trying it out, then making another change, and so on. That's just the way it goes sometimes.

Here's a summary of the process:

Make a model ➡ Test and evaluate ➡ Come up with ideas to improve the product

Now You Should Know Exactly What You're Making

Once you've finished developing your ideas and have a final design, you should have worked out:

1) The sizes of all the parts of the product, and how they fit together.

2) The best materials, tools and other equipment to use (and their availability).

3) The approximate manufacturing time needed to make each item.

4) How much it should cost to manufacture each item.

5) The assembly process — this is important when it comes to planning production (see next page).

Prototypes Help Manufacturers Avoid Big Mistakes

Prototypes are full-size working products made using the right materials and methods. They're made before industrial production to make sure the product is exactly right — so that money isn't wasted:

1) You can test whether the prototype works properly and is safe.

2) You can ask potential end-users (customers) for feedback on the prototype to see whether it meets their needs.

3) If the prototype works well and potential customers like it, a manufacturer would consider going into production.

Practice Questions

1) Nadia is developing her design by producing more detailed sketches.
How will this help her?

2) What are the benefits of modelling your design before making it?

3) Laura wants to make a model of her design for a clock.
Suggest some materials she could use for the model.

4) Explain how CAD/CAM can help at the development stage of designing.

5) Why do manufacturers make prototypes?

Bob decided that his liquorice-based bike frame needed further development.

Planning

In industry, <u>designers</u> usually just <u>design things</u> — they don't make them as well.
So they have to tell the <u>manufacturer</u> exactly <u>what</u> the product is and <u>how</u> to make it.

You Need to Produce a Detailed Production Plan

Before your product can be manufactured you need to produce a <u>detailed plan</u> of <u>exactly</u> how to make the product. It can be a <u>series of written statements</u>, or <u>working drawings</u> and <u>sequence diagrams</u> (see next page). Your plan should include:

1) <u>clear construction details</u> — explain the <u>processes</u> used to make each part and what needs to be <u>prepared</u> before you can start each stage.

2) <u>tools and equipment</u> — which tools and equipment are needed and how they will be <u>used</u>.

3) <u>materials</u> — which materials to use for each part and <u>how much</u> will be needed.

4) <u>sizes</u> — <u>precise</u> measurements of each part in millimetres, and <u>tolerances</u>.

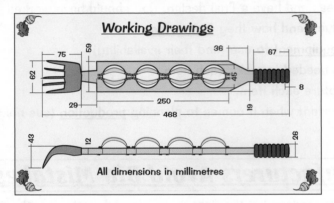

Working Drawings

75   59   36   67
62   45   8
29   250   19
468
43   12   26
All dimensions in millimetres

EXAM TIP
Dimensions must be given in millimetres — you'll lose marks otherwise.

5) <u>quality control instructions</u> — how you will ensure <u>consistency</u>, e.g. using jigs and measuring tools. Include details on when and how you will do <u>quality control checks</u>.

6) <u>time schedules</u> — outlining <u>when</u> you will start each stage and <u>how long</u> it will take.

7) <u>health and safety information</u> — what health and safety <u>precautions</u> you will have to take to be safe when making your product.

Manufacturers Make Plans to Overcome Problems

With Tracey off sick, Brenda and Sue were left playing the "where's the off button" game.

1) <u>Quality Assurance</u> (QA) procedures — e.g. servicing machinery regularly and checking materials as they come in — can help manufacturers avoid problems.

2) But no matter how good procedures are, problems can still arise during production — <u>machines break</u>, suppliers run out of <u>materials</u> and workers go <u>off sick</u>.

3) Manufacturers need to have <u>back-up plans</u> for these situations, e.g. <u>spares</u> of machine parts, <u>other suppliers</u> that can be used and workers trained to <u>cover</u> particular jobs if the usual worker is ill.

Plan to overcome exam problems — do some revision...

The idea is that someone else should be able to use your plan to make your product, so it needs to be <u>really detailed</u>. If it's not, you could be disappointed by the result, and no-one likes to be disappointed...

Planning

You need to plan your work to make the best use of <u>materials</u>, <u>equipment</u> and <u>time</u>.

Use Charts to Help You

You need to work out <u>what order</u> to do things in.

① **Work Order**

This can be produced as a <u>table</u> or <u>flow chart</u>. The purpose of a work order is to plan the <u>sequence</u> of tasks to be carried out. The work order could include details of tools and equipment, quality control stages, safety, and so on.

Day	Process	Tools needed
1	Cut main block of wood	Panel saw
	Cut 4 turnip-holder holes	Drill, fret saw
2	Paint main block of wood	Paint, paint brush

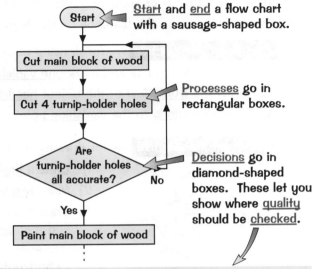

<u>Start</u> and <u>end</u> a flow chart with a sausage-shaped box.

<u>Processes</u> go in rectangular boxes.

<u>Decisions</u> go in diamond-shaped boxes. These let you show where <u>quality</u> should be <u>checked</u>.

The diamond shaped boxes show where you will stop and see if your product looks and works how it should. If you find it doesn't, go back and make sure it's done properly before you move on.

You also need to work out <u>how long</u> each stage will take, and how these times will fit into the <u>total time</u> you've allowed for production. One way to do this is with a Gantt chart:

② **Gantt Chart**

The tasks are listed down the <u>left-hand</u> side, and the <u>timing</u> is plotted across the top. The coloured squares show <u>how long</u> each task takes, and the <u>order</u> they're done in.

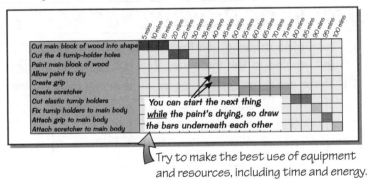

You can start the next thing <u>while</u> the paint's drying, so draw the bars underneath each other

Try to make the best use of equipment and resources, including time and energy.

Practice Questions

1) What things should a <u>production plan</u> include?

2) Why might a manufacturer have <u>QA procedures</u> in their production plan?

3) On a flow chart, how would you show where <u>quality control</u> should take place?

4) Mike is making a table. He has made a Gantt chart of the process.
   a) Why do some of the bars overlap?
   b) How long does the whole process last?
   c) Which is the longest stage? How long does it last?

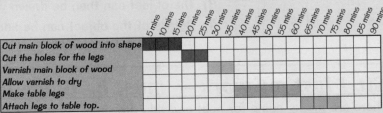

Drawing Techniques

Things get a bit more interesting now. First up, some 3D drawing techniques to get your pulse racing.

Perspective Drawing Uses Vanishing Points

1) Perspective drawing tries to show what something actually looks like — smaller in the distance, larger close up. It does this by using lines that appear to meet at points called vanishing points.

2) These points are in the distance on the horizon line.

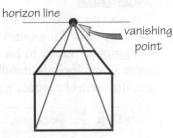

horizon line

vanishing point

One-Point Perspective — for drawing objects head on.

1) Draw a horizon line and mark one vanishing point near the middle.
2) Draw the front view of the object head on.
3) Then draw lines to the vanishing point.

Two-Point Perspective — for drawing objects at an angle.

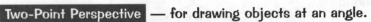

1) Draw a horizon line.
2) Mark two vanishing points near the ends of the horizon line.
3) Draw the object by starting with the front, vertical edge and then projecting lines to the vanishing points.
4) Remember that vertical lines remain vertical and all horizontal lines go to the vanishing points.
5) Rendering can make your drawing look even better.

6) If you can see both surfaces that form a line, draw it thin. If you can only see one surface, draw a thick line. This gives the impression of solidity.

Isometric Drawing Shows Objects at 30°

1) Isometric drawing can be used to show an object in 3D. It doesn't show perspective (things don't get smaller in the distance), but it's easier to get dimensions right than in perspective drawing.

2) There are three main rules when drawing in isometric:

- Draw vertical edges on the object as vertical lines.
- Draw horizontal edges on the object at 30°.
- Check that parallel edges on the object appear as parallel lines on your drawing.

This drawing's been done on isometric grid paper. You could use plain paper and a 30°/60° set square instead.

Crating Can Be Used for 3D Shapes

Crating is where you start by drawing a box — the 'crate' — and gradually add bits on and take bits off till you get the right shape. For example, you can remove sections from a cuboid to make any other 3D shape.

1) When you're sketching a 3D object, it's easier if you imagine it as a basic shape.
2) First draw the basic geometric shape faintly.
3) The object can then be drawn within the box.
4) Details of the object can be added by drawing more geometric shapes on top.

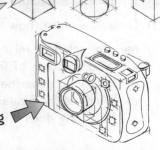

Sir, I lost my work — must be down a vanishing point...

There are marks going for neat and tidy drawings — remember to take a pencil sharpener into the exam.

Drawing Techniques

Assembly drawings and orthographic projection are often used for <u>working drawings</u>.

Assembly Drawings *Show How Things Fit Together*

<u>Exploded views</u> and <u>sectional drawings</u> are two types of assembly drawing.

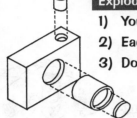

Exploded views

1) You draw the product with <u>each separate part</u> of it <u>moved out</u> as if it's been exploded.
2) Each part of the product is <u>drawn in line</u> with the part it's attached to.
3) Dotted lines show where the part has been <u>exploded from</u>.

Sectional drawings show what the product would look like inside if you cut it in two.

In this diagram the product is imagined to be <u>cut in half</u> through section X,Y.

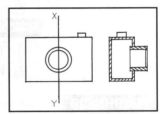

Orthographic Projection *Shows* 2D Views *of a* 3D Object

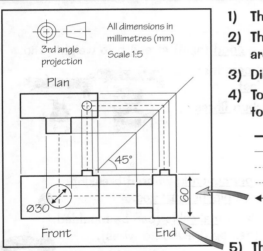

3rd angle projection of camera

All dimensions in millimetres (mm)

Scale 1:5

1) The <u>symbol</u> for <u>3rd angle orthographic</u> projection is:
2) The <u>front view</u>, <u>plan view</u> and <u>end view</u> of the product are drawn <u>accurately to scale</u>.
3) Dimensions are always given in <u>millimetres</u>.
4) To avoid confusion, lines and dimensions must conform to the following <u>British Standards</u> recommendations:

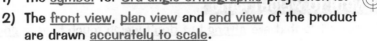

<u>outlines</u>: thick and continuous
<u>projection/construction lines</u>: light and continuous
<u>centre lines</u>: alternate short and long dashes, light
<u>hidden details</u>: short dashes, light
<u>dimension lines</u>: medium and continuous, with solid arrowheads and the dimension written above the line in the middle (or to the left of the line if it's angled or vertical)

5) There's always a <u>gap</u> between the <u>projection lines</u> and the <u>object</u>.

Practice Questions

1) What is a <u>vanishing point</u>?

2) Draw this desk from the front using <u>one-point perspective</u>.

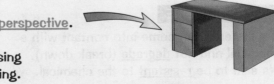

3) Give one advantage and one disadvantage of using <u>isometric drawing</u> rather than perspective drawing.

4) Do an <u>exploded view</u> drawing to show the part of the submarine on the left, including the turrets.

5) In <u>orthographic projection</u>:

   a) What types of lines should be <u>dashed</u>?
   b) What <u>units</u> must the dimensions be given in?

Properties of Materials

Different Materials Have Different <u>Properties</u>

Make sure you're <u>really familiar</u> with all these terms — if you start getting strength and hardness mixed up, or get confused between malleable and ductile, you'll be dropping marks all over the place.

STRENGTH

Strength is the ability to <u>withstand forces</u> without <u>breaking</u>. For example:

1) <u>Tensile strength</u> resists <u>pulling</u> forces — e.g. the rope in a tug-of-war.
2) <u>Compressive strength</u> resists <u>squashing</u> forces — e.g. bridge supports.

HARDNESS

1) This is the ability to withstand <u>scratching</u>, <u>rubbing</u> or <u>denting</u>.
2) It's very important for tools that cut, like <u>files</u> and <u>drills</u>.

TOUGHNESS

1) If a material is <u>tough</u>, it is hard to <u>break</u> or <u>snap</u> — the material changes shape a bit instead.
2) <u>Armour</u> and <u>bulletproof vests</u> need to be tough.

ELASTICITY

1) Elastic materials can <u>stretch and bend</u> and <u>return</u> to their <u>original shape</u>.
2) A <u>spring</u> has good elasticity.

STRENGTH TO WEIGHT RATIO

1) Materials that are <u>strong</u> but <u>don't weigh much</u> have a <u>good</u> (high) strength to weight ratio.
2) This is important for things like <u>spacecraft</u> and <u>racing cars</u> that need to be <u>strong</u> but also <u>light enough</u> to go <u>really fast</u>.
3) Some <u>alloys</u> (p. 22) and <u>composite</u> materials like <u>carbon fibres</u> (p. 28) have a <u>high</u> strength to weight ratio.

EXAM TIP
You get marks for <u>explaining why</u> a particular material is <u>suitable</u> for a product. E.g. 'because it's tough'.

PLASTICITY

1) If a material can <u>change shape permanently</u> without breaking or cracking, it's said to have good <u>plastic qualities</u>.
2) This could mean that the material is <u>malleable</u> (can be moulded, e.g. by hammering) or <u>ductile</u> (can be drawn into wires).

IMPACT RESISTANCE

1) This is the ability to withstand <u>a sudden force</u> without <u>cracking</u>.
2) Most metals have good impact resistance — you can <u>hit them with a hammer</u> without them <u>shattering</u>.

CHEMICAL RESISTANCE

1) If a material can come into contact with a chemical and not <u>degrade</u> (break down), it's said to be <u>resistant</u> to the chemical.
2) <u>Different materials</u> are resistant to <u>different chemicals</u>.

FLEXIBILITY

1) Flexible materials can <u>bend</u>, but don't necessarily return to their normal shape.
2) Electrical wires must be flexible so they can <u>move around</u> to reach different places.

Some live in bungalows, some in semi-detached...

Property jokes aside, you need to be able to say why a material is <u>suitable</u> for a product, and there's only one way you can do that... you really need to get your head around what all these terms mean.

Properties of Materials

THERMAL CONDUCTIVITY

1) Thermal <u>conductors</u> let <u>heat travel</u> through them <u>easily</u>. Thermal <u>insulators</u> don't.
2) <u>Saucepans</u> must be made from good thermal <u>conductors</u>, but their <u>handles</u> are often made from thermal <u>insulators</u>.
3) <u>Metals</u> are good thermal conductors. Plastic and wood are good thermal insulators.

ELECTRICAL CONDUCTIVITY

1) Electrical <u>conductors</u> let electricity <u>travel through them</u> easily. Electrical <u>insulators</u> don't.
2) <u>Electrical wires</u> need to be <u>conductors</u>, but the <u>coating</u> around the wires must be <u>insulating</u>.
3) <u>Metals</u> are good electrical <u>conductors</u>. <u>Plastics</u> tend to be good <u>insulators</u>.

There are Other Factors to Think About Too...

AESTHETICS — HOW IT LOOKS

1) Consider the <u>style</u> of the product. For example, a bowl might require a <u>modern look</u> — you could use glossy white plastic or brushed steel. You'd get a more <u>traditional look</u> by using hardwood or ceramics.
2) Think about how <u>see-through</u> a product should be — e.g. you'd need a fish tank to be <u>transparent</u> (totally see-through), a lamp shade might be <u>translucent</u> (some light passes through it), and storage cupboards should probably be <u>opaque</u> (no light gets through).

SOCIAL AND MORAL ISSUES

1) Consider whether the materials are sourced locally, <u>employing</u> local people.
2) Do the suppliers have <u>good conditions</u> for workers?
3) Think about the <u>environmental impacts</u> of using a material (see page 62-67).

ECONOMICS

1) You need to think about the <u>size</u> of the product — materials like pewter are <u>expensive</u>, but may be a good choice for a small item of jewellery.
2) Whether your product is a <u>one-off</u>, or will be <u>batch</u> or <u>mass produced</u> (see p. 68-69) will make a difference.

If you're making a one-off, hand crafted piece of furniture you might use an expensive piece of hardwood. However, if you're batch-producing cheap furniture, softwood would probably be fine.

Practice Questions

1) Describe what is meant by the following <u>properties</u>:
   a) elastic   b) malleable   c) ductile

2) Suggest a <u>product</u> that needs to be:
   a) flexible   b) hard   c) tough

3) List two products for which <u>strength</u> is important, and say why.

4) Cho is designing the casing for a <u>toaster</u> targeted at people living in <u>swanky new apartments</u>.
   a) Suggest some <u>aesthetic properties</u> that the material she uses should have.
   b) Suggest <u>one working property</u> that the material she uses should have.

Woods and Boards

I love trees. Not only can you climb them but you can turn them into timber and boards.

Softwoods are Evergreen Trees, like Pine

a knot

1) Softwoods include pine, cedar and yew.
2) There are several types of pine but they're all generally pale with brown streaks. Scots pine is fairly strong but knotty. Parana pine is more expensive — it's hard and is best used for interior joinery.
3) Softwoods grow in colder climates and are fast growing — this makes them fairly cheap.

Hardwoods are Deciduous Trees, like Oak

1) Hardwoods include oak, elm, beech and mahogany.
2) They usually grow in warm climates and are slow growing — so they're generally more expensive than softwoods.

mahogany

Natural timber is made when softwood or hardwood trees are made into useful bits of solid wood, e.g. planks and boards. The tree is felled (cut down) and its bark is taken off. Then it can be sliced up in various ways to give different qualities of board — some might warp (bend) less than others.

EXAM TIP
You might have to look at a photo and say what type of wood a product is made from — don't just say 'wood'.

- Many products aren't made from solid timber.
- They're made from manufactured boards instead — plywood, blockboard, MDF, etc.
- Boards are usually available in 2440 x 1220 mm sheets (although you can get smaller sizes e.g. 1220 x 607 mm). The most common thicknesses are 4, 6, 9, 12, 15 and 18 mm.

Plywood — Loads of Layers

Plywood is a man-made board that's very strong for its weight and thickness, compared with solid wood.

1) It's made up of several layers — always an odd number of them.
2) The layers are glued with their grain at 90 degrees to each other — which is why it's so strong.
3) The outside of the board can be finished with a nice veneer (a thin layer of good quality wood) to make it look better.

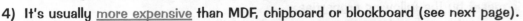

⟹ = Direction of grain

4) It's usually more expensive than MDF, chipboard or blockboard (see next page).
5) You can also buy Marine Ply, which is waterproof and used for boat building.

I'm board — are we nearly there yet...

Make sure you know the difference between hardwood and softwood. Then there's the difference between natural timber and manufactured boards — soon you'll be able to spot them at twenty paces.

Woods and Boards

Blockboard and Laminboard — Blocks in a 'Sandwich'

Blockboard and laminboard aren't as strong as plywood, but they're a cheap substitute, especially when thicker boards are required.

1) Strips of softwood are glued together, side by side, and sandwiched between two veneers. The veneers add strength and make the board look nicer.

2) The outer veneers are glued with their grain at right angles to the grain of the inner core — this makes the board stronger.

Cross-section of blockboard/laminboard.
Veneers
Strips of softwood

3) The softwood used is usually pine or spruce.

4) The thickness of the softwood for laminboard is between 5 mm and 7 mm.

5) The thickness of the softwood for blockboard is greater, at between 7 mm and 25 mm.

6) Because it's cheaper than plywood, it's useful for making things like cupboard doors where a thick board is needed but it doesn't have to be strong.

MDF and Chipboard are Both Made From Wood Chips

Chipboard is made by compressing wood chips together with glue. It's cheap but not very strong, so it's usually used with a stronger veneered surface. It's often used in cheap self-assembly furniture.

Medium density fibreboard (MDF) is made from even tinier wood particles, glued and compressed. It's pretty cheap and has smooth faces that are easy to paint. MDF is often used for shelving units.

Wood Can be Recycled and Reused

Although wood is sustainable (you can plant new trees) it's still a good idea to reuse and recycle timber. This saves on the energy that's needed for processing it into new timber.

1) Wood can be shredded and reused to make things like compost, playground flooring or chipboard.

2) Good quality wood (e.g. undamaged floorboards) can be cleaned up and reused — this is called reclaimed wood.

3) However, manufactured boards are pretty tricky to recycle because they've got glue in them — recycling them is a long process and it's quite expensive.

Practice Questions

1) Give an example of:
   a) a softwood   b) a hardwood

2) Why are hardwoods generally more expensive than softwoods?

3) Blockboard is a type of manufactured board.
   a) Sketch a diagram to show its construction.
   b) List two other types of manufactured board.
   c) Suggest a common use for each type of board you listed in (b).
   d) Why are manufactured boards difficult to recycle?

4) Explain why wood is a sustainable resource.

5) Suggest two ways in which wood can be reused.

Wood Finishes

You're not <u>finished</u> with <u>wood</u> yet...

Prepare <u>Wood</u> Before <u>Applying Finishes</u>

1) Before applying <u>any finish</u>, wood needs to be <u>sanded</u> to a smooth finish using <u>glasspaper</u>. Sand in the direction of the grain.

2) Apply a <u>sanding sealer</u> or <u>primer</u> before sanding wood you're going to <u>varnish</u> or <u>polish</u>. Otherwise, the first coat makes loose wood fibres stick up — and the wood has to be sanded again.

3) Before <u>painting</u>, <u>bare wood</u> needs to be <u>primed</u>. Priming does three useful things:
   - <u>Fills</u> the <u>grain</u> of the timber to give the paint on top a <u>smooth finish</u>.
   - Helps <u>seal</u> the wood, so paint won't <u>soak in</u> and need to be re-applied.
   - Helps the paint to <u>stick better</u> to the wood.

There Are <u>Many Types</u> of <u>Paint</u>

Paints are used to protect wood, when you want to cover up the grain and change its colour. Between <u>each layer</u> of paint you <u>sand lightly</u> in the direction of the grain with fine wire wool or glasspaper.

UNDERCOAT is the first coat of paint (on top of a primer if you've used one, or on old finishes if you're reusing timber).

1) It <u>covers up</u> any previous <u>colours</u> more <u>cheaply</u> than applying extra layers of the final 'topcoat', which is usually a more expensive paint.

2) It helps later layers of <u>paint</u> to <u>stick</u>.

GLOSS PAINTS are <u>hard-wearing</u> and <u>waterproof</u> and come in lots of <u>colours</u>.

1) They're shiny and used for things like interior woodwork.
2) You apply them with a <u>brush</u> or <u>roller</u>, painting in the <u>direction of the grain</u>.

So, deep breath: <u>sand</u>, <u>prime</u>, <u>sand</u>, <u>undercoat</u>, <u>sand</u>, <u>paint</u>, <u>sand</u>, <u>paint</u>.

POLYURETHANE PAINTS are even tougher than gloss paints.

1) They're used for things like children's toys.
2) They're often <u>sprayed</u> on for a <u>smooth finish</u>.

Stains Change the Colour of Wood

1) Stains are either <u>brightly coloured</u> (e.g. red, blue) or <u>wood-coloured</u> (e.g. 'mahogany', 'oak').

2) Wood-coloured stains always <u>darken</u> the timber, but still allow the grain to show. For example, you could use an <u>'oak'</u> stain to make cheap <u>pine</u> furniture look a bit more <u>like hardwood</u>, or to try to <u>match</u> the colour of some other timber.

3) You can get <u>interior</u> stains, e.g. for children's toy blocks, or <u>exterior</u> stains which provide some protection from the <u>weather</u>, e.g. for sheds and fence panels.

4) Stains can be applied with a <u>brush</u>, <u>cloth</u> or <u>spray</u>. The surface should be <u>sanded</u> first, but <u>not primed</u>.

I'm a happy, messy painter — I get overcome with emulsion...

Of course, you never thought paint was just <u>slapped on</u> any old how. But now you know all about <u>sanding</u>, <u>priming</u> and <u>spraying</u>, you'll be extra thrilled next time you see some painted wood. Maybe.

Wood Finishes

Varnish Lets You See the Grain

Many woods (especially hardwoods) have an <u>attractive grain</u> — so you might want to use <u>clear varnish</u> rather than paint as a surface finish. For example, oak furniture is often varnished.

1) Varnish can be <u>coloured</u> or <u>clear</u>, and either <u>gloss</u> (shiny), <u>matt</u> (dull) or <u>satin</u> (in between).

2) <u>Yacht varnish</u> seals the wood and makes it <u>waterproof</u>. It's pretty <u>flexible</u>, so it <u>doesn't crack</u> if the wood <u>moves</u>. So it's good for outdoor uses, e.g. doors and window frames (and yachts).

3) <u>Polyurethane varnish</u> is best for <u>interior</u> uses, e.g. stairs and skirting boards. It's very <u>hard-wearing</u>.

4) For best results, you need to apply <u>two or three coats</u>, <u>sanding</u> lightly <u>between</u> each coat.

Oils Bring Out the Natural Beauty of Wood

Natural oils <u>soak into</u> the wood rather than covering it with a <u>hard layer</u> like varnish — so they retain the <u>feel</u> of wood but provide <u>a bit less protection</u> than varnish.

1) They're <u>waterproof</u> and protect against <u>denting</u>, so for example <u>garden furniture</u> is often protected using <u>teak oil</u>, and <u>cricket bats</u> with <u>linseed oil</u>.

2) The oil is applied with a <u>brush</u> or <u>cloth</u>, and is <u>quick</u> and <u>easy to apply</u>.

Polish Gives a Classy, Traditional Looking Finish

Polish provides the <u>best possible glossy finish</u> for wood, but <u>less protection</u> than other finishes.

FRENCH POLISHING means applying layers of <u>shellac</u> (natural polish from bug cocoons) using a <u>cloth</u>.

1) It's a time-consuming, <u>skilled</u> process that's used for <u>expensive</u> interior <u>furniture</u>.

2) A French-polished surface is <u>easily marked</u>, e.g. with hot cups, but can be <u>repaired</u> by re-polishing.

WAX POLISH can be applied with a <u>cloth</u> or fine <u>wire wool</u>, rubbed in the <u>direction of the grain</u>.

1) The wood needs to be <u>finely sanded</u> between layers.

2) The finish is more durable than French polish, but needs occasional re-buffing.

Practice Questions

1) If you have an attractive piece of wood, why might you want to <u>stain</u>, rather than <u>paint</u> it?

2) Asif is getting ready to paint a wooden toy chest he's just made.
   a) Name two things he should do to it <u>before</u> he <u>paints</u> it.
   b) He pops to the DIY store for some paint. Suggest the <u>two types of paint</u> he should buy.

3) Asif changes his mind and decides to apply a finish that will let the wood grain <u>show through</u>.
   a) What is the most <u>hard-wearing</u> finish that he could use?
   b) What should he do <u>before</u> he <u>sands</u> the toy chest?

4) Ryan has made a <u>picnic table</u> out of really nice <u>oak</u>, and wants to <u>polish</u> it.
   Sarah says he should <u>oil</u> it instead.
   a) Suggest two advantages of oil over <u>polish</u> for finishing a picnic table.
   b) Suggest how Ryan could finish his <u>pine</u> garden trellis so that it will <u>match</u> the oak table.

Metals

Some metals are <u>pure</u> metals and others (alloys) are <u>mixtures</u> of different metals.
Both types of metal can be classified into two basic groups — <u>ferrous</u> and <u>non-ferrous</u>.

Ferrous Metals Contain Iron

1) These are the metals that contain <u>iron</u>.
2) Because of this, almost all of them are <u>magnetic</u>.
3) Examples include <u>mild steel</u>, <u>high-carbon steel</u> and <u>stainless steel</u>.

EXAM TIP
You might need to <u>suggest</u> a suitable metal for a product, so make sure you know what their <u>properties</u> are.

METAL	PROPERTIES	COST	USES
MILD STEEL	Quite <u>strong</u> but <u>rusts</u> easily, and <u>can't</u> be <u>hardened</u> or tempered (see page 29).	<u>Relatively cheap</u>.	car bodies, screws, nuts, bolts, nails, washing machines
HIGH-CARBON STEEL	<u>Harder</u> than mild steel and <u>can</u> be <u>hardened</u> and tempered. But it's <u>not as easy</u> to work and it <u>rusts</u>.	<u>More expensive</u> than mild steel.	drills, files, chisels, saws
STAINLESS STEEL	<u>Hard</u> and <u>won't rust</u>.	<u>More expensive</u> than high-carbon steel (about twice the price of mild steel).	medical equipment, sinks, kettles, cutlery (e.g. knives)

Non-Ferrous Metals Don't Contain Iron (surprise surprise...)

1) If a metal doesn't contain iron, it's <u>non-ferrous</u>.
2) Examples include <u>aluminium</u>, <u>brass</u> and <u>copper</u>.

METAL	PROPERTIES	COST	USES
ALUMINIUM	<u>Lightweight</u> and <u>corrosion-resistant</u> but <u>not</u> as <u>strong</u> as steel.	<u>More expensive</u> than <u>mild steel</u> but <u>cheaper</u> than <u>stainless steel</u>.	aeroplanes, cans, ladders
BRASS	<u>Quite strong</u>, <u>corrosion resistant</u>, <u>malleable</u>, <u>ductile</u> and <u>looks good</u>.	<u>Expensive</u> (about three times the price of aluminium).	door handles, electrical parts
COPPER	Relatively <u>soft</u>, <u>malleable</u> and <u>ductile</u> and a <u>very good electrical conductor</u>.	<u>Very expensive</u> (about six times the price of aluminium).	wiring, pipes

An Alloy is a Mixture

1) An <u>alloy</u> is a <u>mixture</u> of two or more metals, or a metal mixed with another element (e.g. carbon).
2) <u>Steel</u> is made from a mixture of <u>iron and carbon</u>, and <u>brass</u> is made from <u>copper and zinc</u>.
   Different types of steel (e.g. mild steel and stainless steel) also contain varying quantities of other metals, such as chromium — but you don't need to worry about the details.
3) The alloy is a new material — it has <u>different properties</u> and <u>working characteristics</u>.

Ferrous, not ferrets — easy mistake to make...

Not too much to fret over here — <u>ferrous</u> metals, <u>non-ferrous</u> metals and <u>alloys</u>. Make sure you learn what they are, then learn the <u>names</u> and <u>properties</u> for each, and what they can be used for.

Metals

You Can Buy Metals in Loads of Shapes and Sizes

1) Metals are commonly available in a wide range of shapes and sizes, because it can be very difficult to convert one shape to another.

2) This means that the manufacturers can buy roughly the right shape to start working with.

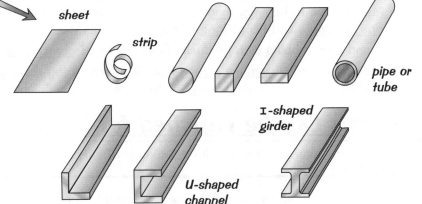

sheet

strip

different shaped bars

pipe or tube

I-shaped girder

angle

U-shaped channel

For example...

this table top was made by cutting out a circle of sheet metal...

...and the chair legs were made from tubes of metal.

Practice Questions

1) What is a ferrous metal?

2) Name two ferrous metals and say which is cheaper.

3) Name two non-ferrous metals and say which is cheaper.

4) Explain why steel is an alloy.

5) Name an alloy other than steel.

6) List five different shapes of metal that are available to manufacturers.

7) Do you think copper would be a suitable material for making the wiring for an electric kettle? Explain your answer.

8) Suggest what material was used to make the head of this hammer. Explain your answer.

9) Explain why stainless steel is useful for making products that are used outdoors.

10) James works for a company that builds aeroplanes. He is designing the wings for a new aeroplane.
   a) Suggest a suitable material for the wings. Explain your answer.
   b) As well as its properties, what else might James need to consider when choosing a suitable material?

Metals

Some metals (e.g. <u>stainless steel</u> and <u>aluminium</u>) don't need a finish, but some (e.g. <u>mild steel</u>) can tarnish or rust without suitable protection. Finishes can also improve the <u>appearance</u> of your product.

Metals Need To be Prepared Before Finishing

1) Metals have to be <u>smoothed</u> first. You can do this by <u>draw-filing</u> — filing in <u>one direction</u>, and filing <u>along</u> rather than across the edge of metal sheets...

2) ...and then rubbing with gradually finer grades of <u>abrasive paper</u> and <u>wet and dry paper</u>.

3) Then you need to <u>remove grease</u> from the surface (by rubbing with a cloth soaked in <u>paraffin</u> or <u>degreaser</u>) — to make sure the finishes will <u>stick properly</u>.

Metals Can be Finished for Protection and Looks

You need to know about a few different kinds of surface finish...

PAINTING

1) A <u>primer</u> such as <u>red oxide</u> or <u>zinc chromate</u> is needed for <u>steel</u> so that later coats of paint can form a strong bond to the surface. You need to remove loose rust and any old flaking paint (with a wire brush) first.

2) After the primer you need a <u>top coat</u>. A range of <u>colours</u> and <u>finishes</u> are available, and can be put on with a brush or spray.

3) <u>Cellulose</u> and <u>acrylic</u> paints are top coats that give a <u>hard</u> and <u>durable finish</u>. They're especially good for <u>outdoor</u> use, e.g. garden gates.

<u>Spray cans</u> give <u>quick</u> and <u>even</u> coverage, but you'll need to <u>mask</u> areas that you don't want to paint.

<u>Brushes</u> come in different shapes and sizes — so you can apply paint <u>accurately</u>.

DIP COATING

1) A metal is <u>heated evenly</u> in an oven and then plunged into <u>fluidised powder</u> (very fine plastic powder that's made to act like a liquid by passing gas through it) for a <u>few seconds</u>.

2) The metal, with this <u>thin coating</u> of plastic, is then put back in the oven and the plastic <u>fuses</u> (joins completely) to the surface.

3) It gives a <u>soft</u>, <u>smooth</u> finish so it's used for things like <u>tool handles</u> and <u>wire racks</u>.

Plastic coating <u>insulates</u> people using the tool from heat or electrical currents.

PLATING

Aahhh, shiny, shiny polished chrome...

1) Metal objects can be coated with a <u>thin layer</u> of another metal by <u>electrolysis</u>.

2) <u>Chromium</u> can be applied to give a <u>shiny</u> finish, e.g. for <u>sink taps</u>, <u>door handles</u> and <u>car bumpers</u>.

3) <u>Zinc</u> gives a <u>corrosion-resistant</u> finish, e.g. for <u>buckets</u> or <u>car bodies</u> (under the paint).

4) <u>Tin</u> gives a <u>non-toxic</u>, <u>corrosion-resistant</u> finish for <u>food cans</u>.

What's the best finish for chef's tools — kitchen zinc...

The thing to remember is that you might need to suggest <u>why</u> a particular finish is <u>suited</u> to a specific task — and how you'd <u>prepare</u> the surface, and how you'd <u>apply</u> the finish. So make sure you can.

Metals

You also need to know a bit about how metals are <u>made</u> and <u>recycled</u>.

Metals Come From the <u>Ground</u>...

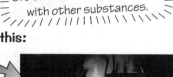
Ore contains the metal along with other substances.

Metal is mined as <u>metal ore</u>. This is <u>processed</u> and <u>refined</u> to make a usable material. The process isn't the same for all metals, but it's often like this:

1) The ore is <u>crushed</u> and heated with other materials in a blast furnace. This process separates the metal from the other substances in the ore. The metal is removed from the blast furnace as <u>molten</u> metal.

2) The <u>molten</u> metal is <u>poured</u> into a casting machine where it's <u>cooled</u> and run through <u>rollers</u> to make blocks. These can then be made into various different <u>shapes</u> (see p. 23).

3) The molten metal from the blast furnace still has some impurities. For some uses you need really pure metal — so sometimes the metal is <u>refined</u> to remove these impurities.

...And This Can <u>Harm</u> the <u>Environment</u>

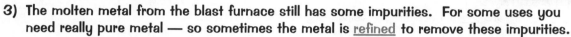

1) Digging up metals <u>disfigures</u> the <u>landscape</u>.

2) Processing and refining metals causes <u>pollution</u> — the <u>chemicals</u> used can be harmful, especially if they get into water sources.

3) <u>Transporting</u> great truckloads of metal ore also causes <u>air</u> and <u>noise</u> pollution.

4) Metal products are often <u>disposed</u> of in <u>landfill</u> sites which isn't ideal — landfill sites become full and more metal needs to be extracted from ore. That's why it's good to <u>recycle</u> and <u>reuse</u> metals instead.

- Recycling uses <u>less energy</u> than extracting new metal and produces <u>less pollution</u>. All good.
- Metals can also be <u>reused</u>. E.g. parts from scrapped cars can be used to fix other cars.
- Metal ores are a <u>finite resource</u> (they'll run out eventually) so recycling and reusing metals helps preserve them.

Practice Questions

1) Most metal products have their surfaces <u>finished</u>. What two things need to be done to metal <u>before</u> a <u>finish</u> is applied?

2) a) Explain why the metal used to make car bodywork is <u>painted</u>.
   b) Give three other surface finishes used on metals.
   c) For each finish in b), give an example of a <u>product</u> for which the finish might be used.

3) What is a metal <u>ore</u>?

4) Explain <u>how</u> metal ore is processed into usable metal.

5) Why are metals sometimes <u>refined</u> after the initial processing?

6) Give three reasons why extracting metals is harmful to the <u>environment</u>.

7) Explain why it's a good idea to <u>reuse</u> and <u>recycle</u> metals.

Plastics

There are two happy families of plastics — thermoplastics and thermosetting plastics. They've got different properties, so don't go mixing them up — some of them are well 'ard.

Thermoplastics are Recyclable and Easy to Shape

Thermoplastics don't resist heat well — they are easy to form into different shapes by heating, melting and moulding. Examples of thermoplastics include:

- Acrylic — hard, shiny and brittle. Used to make baths, signs, etc.
- ABS — tough and durable. Used to make toys, kitchen equipment, etc.
- Expanded polystyrene — lightweight and crumbly. Used to make protective packaging.
- HIPS (High Impact Polystyrene) — rigid. Used for toys, car parts and electrical components.
- LDPE (Low Density Polyethylene) — soft and flexible. Used for packaging, carrier bags, etc.
- HDPE (High Density Polyethylene) — stiff and strong. Used for things like washing-up bowls.
- Nylon — hard-wearing and tough. Used for tool casings, hinges, clothing and rope.
- PVC — soft and flexible. Used as electrical insulation on wires, raincoats, shower curtains, etc.
- uPVC — rigid. Used for window frames, blister packs (for holding pills), etc.
- Polypropylene — flexible and strong. Used for things like toys and garden furniture.

Thermosetting Plastics are Non-Recyclable and Rigid

1) When thermosetting plastics are heated they undergo a chemical change and become hard and rigid. Once you've heated and moulded them to make a product they can't be melted and reshaped again.

2) They resist heat and fire so are used for electrical fittings and pan handles.

3) Examples of thermosetting plastics are epoxy resin and urea-formaldehyde.

EXAM TIP
Don't just write 'plastic' if you're asked to suggest a suitable material — give a specific example, e.g. acrylic.

Choose the Plastic with the Right Properties

So, which type of plastic you use depends on what you want to do with it.

1) For example, thermosetting plastics are often used where there is heat or electricity involved, or when something needs to be really hard.

2) Different types of thermoplastics have different properties — polypropylene will bend without breaking and is used for plastic chairs so they're comfy when you lean back.

Thermoplastics and thermosetting plastics can be bought in many different forms — from powders, granules, pellets and liquids (for processing into finished products), through to films, sheets, rods, tubes and extruded mouldings (complex shapes).

Plastics are Self-Finishing

1) Plastics don't need protective surface finishes because they're very resistant to corrosion and decay.

2) But for a nice appearance, you can use wet and dry paper (silicon carbide paper) to remove scratches from the plastic, and follow that up with a mild abrasive polish or anti-static cream.

3) Or, you could use a buffing machine.

Wet and dry paper — sounds like someone's a bit confused...

So, there are two types of plastic that you need to know about — thermoplastics and thermosetting plastics. Small difference in name, but a pretty big difference in their properties. Best get it learnt...

Plastics

Most Plastics Are Made From Oil

Plastics can be made from substances found in <u>plants</u>. This is quite a new thing though. Most plastics are still made from <u>crude oil</u>.

1) <u>Crude oil</u> is <u>extracted</u> from the ground and taken to a <u>refinery</u>.

2) In the refinery, the oil is <u>processed</u> to make various different substances.

3) Some of these substances are then used to make different types of <u>plastic</u>.

Using Plastics Brings Environmental Problems

1) Crude oil is a <u>finite resource</u> — it's going to run out one day. At the moment we're using it up more and more quickly, to make all the <u>plastic stuff</u> we use (and to make fuels).

2) Turning crude oil into plastic uses a lot of <u>energy</u> (which often comes from burning <u>even more oil</u>).

3) Some plastics (mainly the ones made from plants) are <u>biodegradable</u> — they break down quickly.

4) However, the majority of plastics aren't biodegradable and are disposed of in <u>landfill</u> sites. They're <u>buried</u> and take <u>hundreds of years</u> to <u>degrade</u> (break down). Not so good.

5) So it's good to <u>recycle</u> and <u>reuse</u> plastics as much as possible. It means there's less need to make new plastic from oil.

RECYCLING PLASTICS

1) <u>Thermosetting</u> plastics <u>can't</u> be recycled. (Because they can't be melted and reshaped).

2) <u>Thermoplastics</u> can be <u>cleaned</u>, <u>shredded</u>, <u>melted</u> and made into new products.

3) They have to be <u>sorted</u> into the different types <u>by hand</u> (different types are stamped with different symbols to help). This takes <u>time</u> and people are trying to come up with easier, mechanical ways to sort plastics.

REUSING PLASTICS

1) Some plastic products like <u>milk crates</u> and <u>carrier bags</u> can be used over and over again. Things like <u>printer cartridges</u> can be <u>refilled</u>.

2) Reusing doesn't usually use any <u>energy</u> or new <u>materials</u>. Thumbs up.

Practice Questions

1) a) Give an example of a thermoplastic.
   b) Give an example of a thermosetting plastic.

2) Rachel is designing a <u>saucepan</u>. Suggest a suitable plastic she could use to make the knob on the lid. Explain your answer.

3) List five of the different forms that plastics can be bought in.

4) John is making a child's toy using <u>epoxy resin</u>.
   a) Explain why epoxy resin doesn't need a protective surface finish.
   b) How could John remove any scratches from the surface of the epoxy resin?

5) Outline how plastics are <u>made</u> from crude oil.

6) Why are thermosetting plastics <u>non-recyclable</u>?

7) Describe two <u>environmental problems</u> associated with using plastic.

Changing Properties

Sometimes, with a little <u>tinkering</u>, materials can be made to have loads of <u>great properties</u>...

A <u>Composite</u> <u>is a</u> <u>Combination</u> <u>of</u> <u>Two or More Materials</u>

1) <u>Composite materials</u> are made from <u>two or more materials</u> bonded together.
2) This can make a material with <u>more useful</u> properties than either material alone.
3) For example, you can <u>reinforce plastic</u> with <u>glass fibres</u> or <u>carbon fibres</u> to make a composite that's much <u>stronger</u> than plastic would be by itself.

Glass-Reinforced Plastic (GRP)

1) <u>Glass-Reinforced Plastic</u> (GRP) is a popular choice for large <u>structural</u> items such as some car bodies and boats.
2) GRP is made from <u>glass fibres</u> bonded with <u>polyester resin</u>. Like plastic, it's <u>light</u> and can be moulded, but the glass fibres make it <u>stronger</u>.
3) The glass fibre is available as <u>woven fabric</u>, <u>matting</u> and <u>loose strands</u>.

Carbon Fibre Reinforced Plastic

1) This is similar to GRP, but instead of glass fibres, <u>carbon fibres</u> are used.
2) Carbon-fibre reinforced plastic is even <u>lighter</u>, <u>stronger</u> and <u>tougher</u> than GRP — but it's more expensive.
3) Products made from carbon-fibre composites include <u>protective helmets</u>, <u>racing cars</u>, <u>laptops</u>, <u>sports equipment</u> and <u>bulletproof vests</u>.

Kevlar®

1) KEVLAR® is a man-made substance that can be made into <u>fibres</u>. It's really, really <u>strong</u> — up to <u>five times</u> stronger than <u>steel</u> of the same weight.
2) KEVLAR® is often used as an ingredient in <u>composite materials</u>, because it adds a lot of strength without adding much weight (though it's much <u>more expensive</u> than using glass fibres). For example, it's used in <u>helicopter rotor blades</u>, <u>bulletproof vests</u> and <u>ropes</u>.
3) KEVLAR® is also resistant to <u>abrasion</u> (scraping) and high <u>temperatures</u>, so it's used in things like <u>motorbike clothing</u> and <u>bicycle tyres</u>.

Car-bun fibre is great — it's used to make flatbread trucks...

Ever heard the expression "The whole is greater than the sum of its parts"? It means that when two things work together well, they can be loads better than when they're alone — kind of like composites.

Changing Properties

Heat Treatments Soften or Toughen Metals

Metals can be heat-treated to change their properties. There are three main types of treatment:

1) <u>Annealing</u> — heating the metal and leaving it to <u>cool slowly</u>.
   This makes it softer, more ductile and less brittle.

2) <u>Hardening</u> — heating and rapidly cooling a metal. This makes it, erm... harder.

> The metal is heated till it's <u>red hot</u> then <u>plunged into oil or water</u>.
> This leaves the metal <u>brittle</u>, so hardening is often followed by <u>tempering</u>...

3) <u>Tempering</u> — to make the metal <u>tougher</u> and less likely to break.

> When <u>steel</u> is tempered, it's first <u>cleaned</u> (to make it bright in
> appearance) and then <u>gently heated</u>. As it gets hotter, it gradually
> changes colour — and the colour shows <u>how tough</u> it's become.

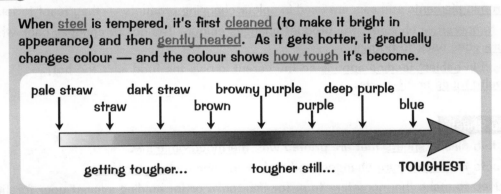

pale straw   dark straw   browny purple   deep purple
      straw   brown   purple   blue

getting tougher...   tougher still...   **TOUGHEST**

Practice Questions

1) What is a <u>composite material</u>?

2) One example of a composite is carbon-fibre reinforced plastic.
   a) How does carbon-fibre reinforced plastic compare to ordinary plastic?
   b) Why might glass-reinforced plastic be used <u>instead</u> of carbon-fibre reinforced plastic?
   c) Give two <u>uses</u> of carbon-fibre reinforced plastic.
   d) Give two <u>uses</u> of glass-reinforced plastic.

3) Give a <u>property</u> of KEVLAR® that would make it useful in:
   a) motorbike clothing
   b) helicopter rotor blades

4) Explain the differences between <u>annealing</u> and <u>hardening</u>.

5) a) What is the name of the process used to <u>toughen</u> metal?
   b) Outline what happens during the process.

Smart and Modern Materials

Using smart materials, we can now make products that you couldn't have dreamed of a few years ago...

'Smart' Materials React to Their Environment

Smart materials are materials whose properties change when their environment changes.

Nitinol

1) Nitinol is a shape memory alloy.

2) It can be easily shaped when cool, but returns to a 'remembered' shape when heated above a certain temperature.

3) So if your glasses are made of nitinol and you accidentally bend them, you can just pop them into a bowl of hot water and they'll jump back into shape.

Percy wished his glasses were made of nitinol.

Thermochromic Pigments

1) Thermochromic pigments and inks are used in colour changing products — they react to temperature.

2) When the temperature changes, the product changes colour. The colour changes back when the temperature goes back to normal.

3) They're used in babies' feeding spoons so the parent knows the food isn't too hot, and in novelty mugs and t-shirts.

Thermochromic Sheets

1) These are thin plastic sheets that are printed with thermochromic ink.

2) The ink reacts to temperature changes, and makes the sheet change colour.

3) They are used to make thermometers (e.g. for fish tanks or for holding against your forehead). Another use is for indicators on batteries to show the remaining charge — a resistor heats up if there's any charge left in the battery, causing the sheet on top to change colour.

Polymorph

1) This is a plastic that becomes easily mouldable when it's heated, allowing its shape to be changed.

2) Polymorph comes as small plastic granules which melt at 60 °C. They can then be moulded by hand into the desired shape, which becomes rigid once it's cooled.

3) If the material is heated to 60 °C again, the polymorph can be shaped into a different form.

4) Polymorph is used to make models, prototypes and moulds.

Carly was afraid she might begin to expand if she went into the water.

Hydromorph Plastics

1) These are plastics that gradually expand when they're put in water. When they're dried out, they shrink back to their original size.

2) You buy them as two separate liquids. You mix them together, pour the mixture into a mould, and leave it to set.

3) They are an easy way to change the size of 3D models. Make a cast of your model by pouring liquid hydromorph around it. When the cast has set, put it in water, and hey presto — you've got a bigger mould to make an enlarged copy of your model.

Smart materials, eh — back in my day...

Blimey, substances that remember their shape, inks that change colour with temperature and plastics that can change shape or size. Smart materials certainly merit their name — they're definitely pretty clever.

Smart and Modern Materials

Modern Materials are...well, Modern

These materials might not be <u>smart</u> in the same way as the ones on the previous page, but they're still <u>pretty clever</u> if you ask me...

1) <u>Flexiply</u>® is a really <u>flexible plywood</u> sheet which can be <u>bent</u> into many different shapes. It's used to make things like <u>furniture</u> and <u>curved shop counters</u>. It's much <u>easier</u> to use than having to bend normal plywood sheets using <u>steam</u>. To get a rigid but curvy shape, <u>glue together</u> two or more sheets.

2) <u>Flexi-veneer</u>® is a really <u>flexible wood veneer</u> — a veneer is a thin sheet of wood glued to doors or furniture to give a decorative finish. Flexi-veneer® can be bent in <u>any direction</u> unlike traditional veneers — which makes it much <u>easier</u> to <u>cut</u> and <u>handle</u> without it <u>splitting</u>.

3) <u>Hexaboard</u> is a <u>light</u> and <u>strong</u> board made from plywood with a <u>plastic laminate</u> on both faces. It has a distinctive <u>hexagonal</u> pattern in the plastic. It has good <u>impact resistance</u>, so it's used to make <u>protective cases</u> — e.g. flight cases for musical instruments.

4) <u>Anodised aluminium sheet</u> is aluminium sheet that has had its protective surface layer <u>thickened</u> using an <u>electrical current</u>. This makes the surface <u>harder</u> and more <u>resistant to corrosion</u>. It can also <u>absorb</u> permanent <u>dye</u> to make <u>coloured products</u>. Anodised aluminium is used to make loads of stuff including aircraft parts, cooking pans and window frames.

5) <u>Alu composite sheet</u> is made by sandwiching a <u>thermoplastic sheet</u> between two thin layers of pre-painted aluminium. This makes a very <u>rigid</u>, <u>lightweight</u> and <u>weather-resistant</u> sheet. It can be produced in many <u>different colours</u> and given different <u>metal</u>, <u>wood</u> or <u>stone effect</u> finishes. It's mainly used to make signs or cover the outside of buildings.

But New Materials Aren't the Answer to Everything

Although smart materials and other modern materials can do really <u>clever</u> things, they do have downsides:

1) They're often much more <u>expensive</u> than standard materials, because of the <u>high-tech machinery</u> needed to produce them.

2) Many of these materials are also less <u>sustainable</u> — they use up more <u>finite resources</u>, and more <u>energy</u> is needed to make them. For example, <u>hexaboard</u> is <u>less sustainable</u> than <u>regular plywood</u> because <u>oil</u> is needed to make the <u>plastic laminate</u>.

3) <u>Smart</u> and <u>modern</u> doesn't always mean <u>better</u>. Often you can get the same results using a <u>simpler</u> option.

Dave wished his new smart robot wasn't quite so smart.

Practice Questions

1) Nitinol is a '<u>smart</u>' material.
   a) What is a 'smart' material?
   b) What special <u>property</u> does nitinol have?
   c) Suggest one <u>use</u> of nitinol.
   d) Give another example of a 'smart' material.

2) Suggest a <u>modern material</u> that you could use to make:
   a) A road sign
   b) A curved information board

3) What <u>two things</u> should you check <u>before you decide</u> to use a smart or modern material?

Nanotechnology

Nanotechnology means working with materials on a really small scale.

Materials Made of Nanoparticles Have Useful Properties

1) Nanoparticles are really really really really tiny lumps of material, so tiny that you could fit about a thousand of them into the width of one of these hairs.

2) Nanoparticles of a substance often have different properties from the normal substance. This means materials made from (or containing) nanoparticles may have very different properties from normal materials.

3) For example, normal copper can usually be bent fairly easily. However, copper made up of copper nanoparticles is super hard and can't be bent.

4) Many new products have been made using nanoparticles. There are two types that you need to know about — products with coatings of nanoparticles, and products containing nanocomposites (where nanoparticles are combined with other materials).

Nanoparticle Coatings Give Surfaces Useful Properties

1) Self-cleaning glass can be made using a coating of nanoparticles. When sunlight hits the glass, nanoparticles react with ultraviolet light to break down dirt on the surface so it's easily washed off by rain. It's useful for making windows for places that are difficult to clean.

2) Water-repellent coatings can be made using nanotechnology. They make water on surfaces form into beads and roll off, instead of soaking in. It makes glass and tiles easy to clean, and helps to prevent wood from warping (twisting) and going rotten.

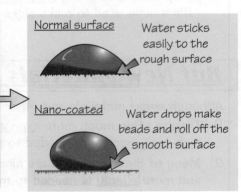

Normal surface — Water sticks easily to the rough surface

Nano-coated — Water drops make beads and roll off the smooth surface

3) Anti-graffiti paints are really hard to paint over. They contain nanoparticles of water-repellant and oil-repellant chemicals, so spray paint doesn't stick — it drips off or can be removed really easily.

4) Antibacterial coatings contain nanoparticles of a substance that kills bacteria. They're useful for surfaces like hospital door handles and toilet flush handles to stop diseases spreading.

Foot warmers, shopping scooters — no, that's nanatechnology...

Minute. Microscopic. Miniscule. Unbelievably incredibly fantastically little. The size of nanoparticles? No, the fun of exams. Still, learn this stuff and even if they're not fun, they don't have to be horrible.

Nanotechnology

Nanocomposites are Used to Strengthen Products

Nanoparticles can also be combined with other materials to make nanocomposites with very desirable properties. For example:

Mavis was only interested in Reg's new racquet.

1) Carbon nanotubes (really thin tubes of carbon) can be added to carbon fibre (strands of carbon embedded in resin) to make bike frames that are still really strong but are much lighter than normal frames.

2) Tennis racquet frames can also be strengthened by the addition of carbon nanotubes, making strong but light racquets.

There was no chance that competitive dad was going to let Daisy use his nanocomposite club.

3) Carbon nanotubes can be added to the heads of golf clubs as well. This reduces their weight (but not their strength), allowing the golfer to swing the club faster and so hit the ball harder.

4) Although nanocomposites are really useful and can improve many products, they are often very expensive to make.

Some People are Worried Though...

Some people are worried that nanotechnology might have long-term risks — but because it's so new there's no good evidence either way.

1) Nanoparticles could be harmful to the environment — because they're really, really small and lightweight, they could be carried into the atmosphere or contaminate water sources.

2) This could make it difficult and expensive to dispose of nanomaterials safely.

Practice Questions

1) What is a nanoparticle?

2) Bill has designed a new toy. Suggest how he might have used a nanomaterial in his design to make the product safer for children.

3) Give an example of a nanotechnology product that could be used to:
   a) stop wood from going rotten.
   b) make glass buildings easier to maintain.

4) Give two examples of products that have been improved by making them from a nanocomposite containing carbon nanotubes.

5) Why are some people worried about the environmental consequences of using nanoparticles?

Section 2 — Materials and Components

Fixtures and Fittings

From the wonders of nanotechnology... to good old <u>nails</u> and friends. You need to know these <u>pre-manufactured components</u> and the kinds of things they're used for.

Nails, Screws and Bolts Come in Standard Sizes

These components are used to <u>fix</u> the parts of a product <u>together</u> — it's important to use the <u>right sort</u> to make sure that the job <u>looks good</u> and <u>holds together properly</u>.

NAILS (p. 49) are a <u>quick</u>, <u>permanent</u> fixing for <u>wood</u>. They are put in with a hammer or nail gun.

1) They're <u>not very pretty</u>, so they're usually used where the fixing <u>won't be seen</u>.
2) They're used to fix <u>fence panels</u>, and join the <u>backs of wardrobes</u>, for example.

SCREWS (p. 48) are often used as <u>temporary fixings</u>, or with <u>glue</u> as <u>permanent fixings</u>.

1) The screw thread <u>grips</u> the material, so they make a <u>strong</u>, <u>tight fixing</u> in wood, metal and plastic.
2) They are used for lots of jobs, e.g. for access to the batteries in <u>children's toys</u>, <u>self-assembly furniture</u>, fixing <u>shelves</u> and <u>mirrors</u> to walls, and fixing <u>hinges</u> to doors.

NUTS AND BOLTS (p. 48) are used as <u>temporary fixings</u> for joining <u>thin materials</u> like sheets of metal.

1) They're only useful if you can get to <u>both sides</u> of the materials you're joining.
2) They're used to join parts of <u>machinery</u>, e.g. in cars and bridges, and to hold <u>moving parts</u>, e.g. in play swings.

Temporary fixings are designed to be taken apart, and put back together if necessary. Permanent fixings are... permanent.

Knock Down Fittings Are Used to Make Furniture

Knock down fittings (see p. 48) are <u>non-permanent</u> fittings that allow furniture to be <u>assembled</u> and <u>taken apart easily</u>. They're quicker to use than permanent joints (see p. 50) and are used a lot in <u>flat-pack furniture</u>. There are different types for <u>different joints</u> — and you need to know them all.

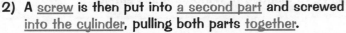

SCAN FITTINGS (sometimes called BARREL NUT AND BOLTS)

1) A <u>cylinder</u> with a <u>screw thread inside</u> is put into a ready-made <u>hole</u> in a part.
2) A <u>screw</u> is then put into <u>a second part</u> and screwed <u>into the cylinder</u>, pulling both parts <u>together</u>.
3) It's used with materials like <u>plywood</u> where the screw wouldn't <u>grip</u> well (e.g. in tables to attach the legs to the frame).

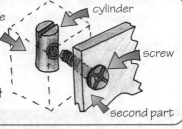

part (with ready-made hole for the cylinder) — cylinder — screw — second part

CAM LOCKS

1) A <u>disk</u> with a <u>slot</u> in fits into one part. A <u>peg</u> is screwed into a second.
2) When the parts are <u>pushed together</u>, the peg is pushed into the slot in the side of the disk. <u>Turning</u> the disk <u>grabs</u> the <u>peg</u> and pulls the parts <u>tightly together</u>.
3) It's used to join the <u>sides</u> of cabinets to the <u>top</u>. It looks quite <u>neat</u> (it's mostly hidden <u>inside</u> the parts).

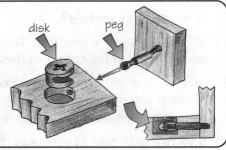

disk — peg

What do Brazilian carpenters use — Amazon nails...

As well as being able to <u>identify</u> these pre-manufactured components, you need to be able to suggest a <u>use</u> for each of them. Have a poke round at home — you'll probably find something using each one.

Fixtures and Fittings

Some More Knock Down Fittings...

SINGLE and TWO-PIECE BLOCKS (sometimes called MODESTY BLOCKS)

1) These are <u>plastic blocks</u> used to join <u>parts</u> at <u>right angles</u>.

2) They have holes in them to fit <u>screws</u> through, and screw into ready-made <u>holes</u> in the parts being joined.

3) <u>Two-piece blocks</u> are first screwed into the parts, and then joined together with a <u>bolt</u>, making the joint straight and strong.

4) They can be easier to attach in <u>tight corners</u> than single piece blocks, and can be <u>undone</u> if required.

5) They're often found holding up <u>shelves</u> in wardrobes.

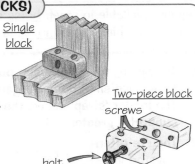

Single block

Two-piece block

screws

bolt

LEG PLATES (sometimes called CORNER PLATES)

1) They're metal plates that are used to join <u>legs</u> onto <u>table frames</u>.

2) The <u>ends</u> of the plate screw into the <u>frame</u>. Then the <u>leg</u> is joined to it using a <u>wing nut and bolt</u>.

3) They can easily be <u>taken apart</u>.

4) They end up <u>hidden</u> under the table top.

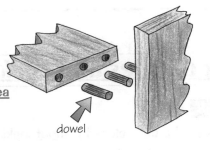

table leg

wing nut

DOWELS

1) Dowels are <u>wooden rods</u> that are pre-cut to length.

2) They're used in <u>dowel joints</u> (see p. 50). Holes are drilled into the <u>ends</u> and <u>sides</u> of <u>parts</u>, and the dowels fit into them like a <u>peg</u>.

3) They're usually used with <u>glue</u>, and give more <u>contact area</u> to the joint to make it stronger. The dowels have little <u>channels</u> in them to make space for the glue. Gluing makes them a <u>permanent fixing</u>.

4) They're often used to attach <u>shelves</u> to cabinets.

dowel

Practice Questions

1) Apart from knock down fittings, name a <u>component</u> that could be used to fix parts of a product together temporarily.

2) What <u>components</u> could be used to attach the blades to this ornamental windmill so that they could <u>spin</u>?

3) Why are <u>knock down fittings</u> often used to make flat-pack furniture?

4) Name a <u>fitting</u> used to join legs onto table frames.

5) Name a <u>fitting</u> used to attach shelves to cabinets.

Fixtures and Fittings

Here are some more lovely <u>components</u> to get your teeth into. Watch out though — these ones <u>move</u>.

There Are Four Main Types of Hinge

<u>Hinges</u> are available in <u>steel</u>, <u>brass</u> and <u>nylon</u>, and can be <u>coated</u> to match a piece of furniture.
The part of the hinge that <u>moves</u> is called the <u>knuckle</u>.

1) <u>Tee hinges</u> are often used outside for things like shed doors or garden gates. The longer 'strap' allows the hinge to support a greater weight.

2) They're often covered in <u>black enamel</u>.

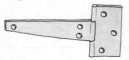

1) <u>Butt hinges</u> are the most common type of hinge used for doors.

2) One part of the hinge is <u>set into</u> the door and the other part is set into the frame.

3) They're available in <u>brass</u> or <u>steel</u>.

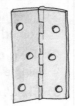

1) <u>Pivot hinges</u> allow you to lift a door off its frame.

2) The hinge is made from two parts that fit together. One part is screwed to the <u>door</u> and the other is screwed to the <u>door frame</u>.

1) <u>Flush hinges</u> are screwed directly onto the surface of the wood, so they're easier to fit than butt hinges.

2) They're usually used for <u>lightweight jobs</u>.

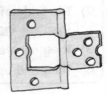

Most Catches and Locks are Made from Steel or Brass

CATCHES

<u>Catches</u> hold a door closed <u>without</u> locking.

1) There are various types of catches available. Here are a few.

2) They can be made out of <u>brass</u>, <u>steel</u> and various <u>plastics</u>.

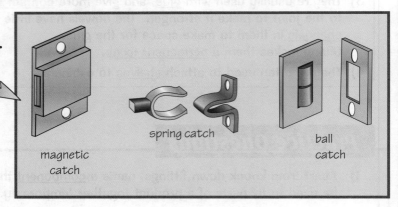

magnetic catch

spring catch

ball catch

LOCKS

Locks need to be <u>strong</u> so they tend to be made from <u>steel</u>, <u>plated steel</u> or <u>brass</u>.

1) <u>Cupboard locks</u> are screwed to the inside <u>edge</u> of cupboard doors. Turning the key moves the <u>bar</u> out.

2) <u>No cutting</u> is required when fitting the lock.

Jo could only fix 21 doors shut — it was a catch-22 situation...

It's no use pretending to be mad to try and get out of your exams... wanting to get out of your exams will prove that you're sane. Never mind, remember the <u>uses</u> of these <u>components</u> and you'll fly through.

Fixtures and Fittings

Drawer Slides and Handles Make Drawers Open Easily

DRAWER SLIDES

Drawer slides (or drawer runners) are fitted to furniture to make drawers slide open smoothly.

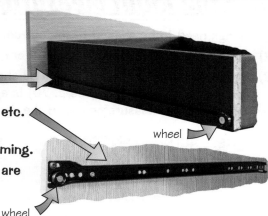

wheel

1) One part screws to the outside of the drawer — it usually has nylon wheels that run along the other part, which is screwed onto the inside of the cupboard, desk, etc.

2) They also stop the drawer being pulled out too far, and can have a soft-close mechanism to stop them slamming.

3) Most drawer slides are made from metal, although there are cheaper plastic ones that slide without wheels.

4) Drawer slides are often used in flat-pack furniture.

wheel

Knobs come in a range of shapes and sizes.

KNOBS AND HANDLES

These are used to open, shut or lock doors or drawers.

1) The right handle or knob can finish off a door nicely for a high-quality appearance. They're usually screwed on.

2) Some are ergonomically shaped to fit hands comfortably. Others are just designed to look good.

Practice Questions

1) Jack is making a door for a small kitchen cupboard. What type of hinge should he use?

2) Name the two types of hinge below:

a)

b)

3) Both butt hinges and pivot hinges can be used for doors. Give one advantage of using a pivot hinge.

4) Suggest a suitable material for making a lock. Explain your answer.

5) What are catches used for?

6) Give two advantages of using drawer slides.

7) Rob makes some knobs out of oak to attach to the doors of his cabinet. He wants to glue them on. Suggest a better way of attaching them.

Preparing and Measuring Materials

It's important to <u>prepare</u>, <u>measure</u>, <u>mark out</u> and <u>test</u> your materials <u>before</u> you start making your product.

Use the Right Measuring Tools

1) Things need to be shaped to the correct size — so measure <u>carefully</u>.

2) Different measuring <u>tools</u> have different levels of <u>accuracy</u>.

3) <u>How</u> accurate you need to be will be shown by the <u>tolerance</u> in the manufacturer's specification. <u>Tolerance</u> (see p. 70) is a <u>margin of error</u> — there's an <u>upper</u> and <u>lower limit</u> for measurements. If the component fits inside the limits, it's <u>accepted</u>.

Length is usually measured in mm.

STEEL RULE
— used to measure <u>length</u>.

VERNIER CALLIPERS
— used to measure <u>thickness</u> or <u>diameter</u>.
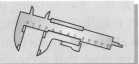

DIVIDERS — used to <u>roughly</u> measure the length of a <u>curved line</u> by "walking" the dividers along the line (with the points a known distance apart).

COMBINATION SQUARE — used to check things are <u>level</u>, measure <u>angles</u>, and to find the <u>centre of circles</u>.

TRY SQUARE — used to measure <u>90° angles</u> on wooden objects. An engineer's square is used for metal or plastic.

Templates can be drawn round to make accurate copies of the same shape — saving you from measuring over and over again (see p. 52).

There are Many Different Tools for Marking Out...

1) <u>Marking out</u> is making a mark so you know where to <u>cut</u>, <u>drill</u> or <u>assemble</u>.

2) This might be as basic as using a <u>pencil</u> on a piece of <u>wood</u> (you shouldn't use a pen as it seeps into the wood and you can't get it out) or a <u>felt tip</u> on a piece of <u>plastic</u> — but there are lots of other ways:

SCRIBER
— used like a pencil but it <u>scratches</u> a <u>mark</u> into metal and plastic.

MARKING KNIFE
— used to <u>score</u> lines in wood (it cuts the fibres to stop them <u>splitting</u> during sawing).

ODD LEG CALLIPERS
— marks a line <u>parallel</u> to an edge.

MARKING GAUGE
— <u>scratches a line</u> in wood <u>parallel</u> to an edge.
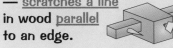

SLIDING BEVEL
— can be set at any angle to <u>guide</u> a marking knife.

ENGINEER'S BLUE and **MARKING BLUE** are dyes you put on metal so any scribe marks show up better.

A <u>try square</u> or <u>engineer's square</u> (see above) are also often used when marking out.

How do you grade DT exams — with a marking gauge...

There are lots of different tools on this page — and you need to know them. Oh, and another thing... as a wise man once said to me — always <u>measure</u> things out <u>twice</u>, then you'll only have to <u>cut once</u>.

Preparing and Measuring Materials

...And When You're Marking Out, Remember...

1) Keep the marks as <u>thin</u> as possible — otherwise your cutting might be <u>inaccurate</u>...
2) ...and remember to <u>get rid</u> of the marks when you've finished so it doesn't look <u>untidy</u>.
3) If possible, mark out on a surface that the user <u>won't see</u> — for example on the back of a door, or the inside surface of a box.
4) When you cut, always do it on the <u>waste side</u> of the line so it doesn't end up too <u>small</u>. If it's a bit big, you can always <u>file</u> it down to size — but if it's too small you'll have to <u>cut it again</u>.

The waste side

Make Pilot Holes with Centre Punches and Bradawls

<u>CENTRE PUNCH</u> — you hit it with a hammer to make a little dent where you're going to drill (a pilot hole) — it stops the drill slipping. It's used on <u>metal</u> and <u>plastic</u>.

<u>BRADAWL</u> — makes a little hole to start off drilling or to help put in screws. You just press it into the material. It's used on <u>wood</u> and <u>plastic</u>.

Check You've Done it Correctly

1) <u>Limit gauges</u> are made to check <u>sizes</u> quickly — rather than measuring each item with a rule (see page 71 for more on limit gauges and <u>quality control testing</u>). It's probably only worth doing if you're making <u>lots</u> of the same product, and need them all the <u>same size</u>.
2) <u>Callipers</u> can also be used to quickly check the size of an item. You set them to the right size using a <u>rule</u>.

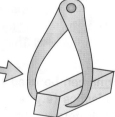

Practice Questions

1) What are <u>vernier callipers</u> used for?
2) Why is it important to <u>mark out</u> materials before cutting them?
3) Caroline needs to cut a piece of wood along a 45° angle to make a picture frame. Name <u>two</u> marking out <u>tools</u> she could use, and explain what she would use them for.

4) Thomas is going to use a scriber to mark out his material before he cuts it. Suggest <u>two things</u> that he should do to help make sure his cutting will be <u>accurate</u>.
5) Sikander is building a wooden bookcase.
   a) How might a <u>bradawl</u> be useful to him?
   b) Why wouldn't he use a <u>centre punch</u>?

Hand Tools

Hand tools are, well, tools that work by hand (i.e. not machine tools or power tools).

Saws are the Main Cutting Tools

There are different saws for different materials. Saws with lots of little teeth close together (fine pitch) are usually for hard materials and saws with bigger teeth further apart (coarse pitch) are for soft materials. Using the wrong saw could damage the material (or hurt you — it could 'jump' or catch unexpectedly).

Rip saw — for cutting wood along the grain

Tenon saw — for making straight cuts in small pieces of wood

Hacksaw — for metals and plastics

Coping saw — for cutting curves in wood or plastic

1) Try to use the whole length of the blade so that some teeth don't wear out faster than others.
2) Don't press too hard or the saw might jam in the material. This will damage the blade, the material or even you when you try to pull it out.
3) Rough edges from sawing can be tidied up by sanding or planing.

Planes and Files are Used for Shaping and Smoothing

1) A bench plane has an angled blade that shaves off thin layers of material. It's used on wood for removing material (shaping).

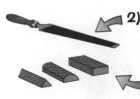

2) Files are used for metal and plastic. They have hundreds of small teeth to cut away at a material. Different 'cuts' make them suitable for different processes: rough cuts are for removal of material, fine cuts are for finishing (final smoothing). They come in different profiles — to make different shapes.

3) Surforms can be used to shape soft materials like wood, foam and some plastics (e.g. expanded polystyrene). They look a bit like cheese graters — they have a metal grating surface with holes in it to let the shavings through. You can get flat and curved surforms.

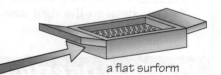
a flat surform

above

below

blade

4) Spokeshaves are used to shape wood into curves — they're used to make things like chair legs. They're basically a blade with two handles.

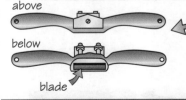

When you're using any hand tools:

- Make sure the object you're working on can't move — hold it firmly in a bench hook, vice or clamp.
- Keep your fingers out of the way.
- Be aware of the exposed blade, and always carry it safely.
- It's a good idea to wear goggles to stop shavings getting in your eyes.

My file slipped — now my finger is saw...

Sounds obvious, but saws need to be kept sharp — either by sharpening or replacing the blade.
Shears are another cutting tool — they're a bit like scissors, but for cutting thin plastic and sheet metal.

Hand Tools

Drills Make Holes (no kidding...)

1) To help you drill in the right place, you can make a pilot hole first (see p. 39).

(see p. 39)

2) Depending on how hard the material is, you can do the actual drilling with a brace, a hand drill or a power drill.

3) All drills work by rotating a drill bit against the material.

brace

hand drill

Twist bits are used to drill small holes in wood, metal or plastic.
High speed steel (HSS) twist bits are used on metals and plastics.

Flat bits are used on wood and plastics to drill large, flat-bottomed holes.
Forstner bits make similar holes, but can only really be used on machine drills.

Countersink bits make holes for screw heads to sit in.

Hole saws are a bit like round saws that are used in a drill.
They're used to make big holes in thin material.

4) Drills can get really hot, so be careful when taking them out of the material.

Chisels are Used for Shaping

Chisels are used to cut away and shape wood and metal.

1) Wood chisels come in different profiles for making different shapes. You hit them with a mallet.

2) Gougers are used for sculpting.

3) For metal, you need cold chisels. These are hit with a hammer.

4) Never chisel towards you — the chisel could slip and hit you. Always strike it away from you, but make sure there's no one else close by who might get hurt.

5) Keep the blade sharp (blunt blades are more likely to slip) — but keep your hands away from the cutting edge. Carry chisels by your side and make sure they don't roll off the bench.

Practice Questions

1) Name a type of saw that is used for cutting metals.

2) What is a coping saw used for?

3) Paul wants to remove a thin layer of wood from the bottom of a door he is fitting. Suggest a tool that he could use to do this.

4) Name these two types of drill bit, and say what they're used for.

5) Suggest a tool suitable for:
   a) sculpting wood
   b) shaping metal

Power and Machine Tools

After the delights of hand tools, you now get on to the really exciting stuff — power tools.

Safety *is Really* Important *with* Power Tools

1) Before using power tools, do a visual check for any loose connections and run your hand along the lead to check for any cuts in the insulation (when it's switched off, of course). Check that the blade or drill bit or whatever is attached correctly and tightly.

2) You can use an RCD (Residual Current Device) to help prevent electric shocks. The power tool plugs into the RCD, which you plug into the socket. If you accidentally cut through the lead of the power tool, the RCD cuts off the electricity supply straight away.

3) Wear a mask or fit an extraction hose if the tool's going to produce a lot of dust. Always wear safety glasses and make sure clothing can't get caught.

4) Clamp your work down firmly so it can't slip or move.

5) Make sure you know where the stop buttons are before you start.

6) When you've finished, make sure the tool has stopped moving before you put it down.

Routers, Planers *and* Jigsaws *are Really* Useful

1) Hand-held routers are machines that have a spinning cutting tool that cuts away wood. They're used to make features like slots, grooves and fancy edges.

2) A router is usually used with a fence (see page 53) — a thing that guides the router and keeps it in the right position.

3) You can get different cutting tools to make different shapes.

1) A planer is used like a bench plane to remove shavings of wood — either to reduce the material to the required size, or for rough shaping.

2) The advantage of a power planer is that it takes much less effort and is much faster — but it's not as accurate as a bench plane.

3) Before you start, check the blades are sharp and replace them if not.

4) Don't start with the cutting tool on the wood — rest the flat front base on the wood and start to push it forward when it reaches full speed.

5) Make sure you're well-balanced and use two hands to hold it — one on the front handle and one on the trigger switch.

1) A jigsaw has interchangeable blades and variable speeds.

2) You can make straight or curved cuts in all materials, but it's quite slow. A fence helps you make straight cuts.

3) Make sure the blade is secured tightly and the correct type of blade is installed for the material. The teeth should face the front of the saw, and you should push it forwards (away from you). Don't start cutting until the blade is at full speed.

It took me ages to put my jigsaw together...

These are the type of tools that you might get to use at school — so make sure you know how to use them safely. They might come up in a safety-related question in the exam too, so it's worth learning.

Power and Machine Tools

Milling Machines _Remove_ Thin Layers _of Material_

1) A <u>milling machine</u> is used to remove material one <u>thin layer at a time</u> to produce the required size or shape.

2) It can also be used to make a surface <u>absolutely flat</u>.

3) It can produce a very <u>accurate finish</u>.

4) Before you start, make sure your work is <u>clamped firmly</u>, and that all the <u>safety guards</u> are in place.

5) Check that the cutting tools are <u>sharp</u>, and that the machine is set to the correct <u>cutting speed</u> and <u>depth</u>.

Lathes _Are For_ Turning

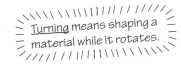
Turning means shaping a material while it rotates.

1) <u>Lathes</u> come in two types — <u>wood lathes</u> and <u>engineers' lathes</u> (also known as centre lathes, and are for working metal). They're used to 'turn' materials, to make objects like these.

2) A piece of material is <u>held</u> and <u>rotated</u> by the lathe, while a <u>tool</u> or <u>bit</u> is pressed onto the material to cut it.

3) <u>Before</u> using a lathe, check that all the <u>guards</u> are in place and aren't <u>cracked</u>.

4) Keep your <u>hands away</u> from <u>moving pieces</u>.

5) Make sure the lathe is set to <u>rotate</u> at the correct <u>speed</u> for the material being cut and the cutting tool being used.

6) Make sure the material is held <u>tightly</u> and <u>straight</u>. If you're turning a <u>long</u> piece of wood or metal, it needs to be held securely at <u>both ends</u> to stop it <u>wobbling</u>.

Practice Questions

1) Give <u>two safety precautions</u> that need to be taken when working with power tools.

2) Susan is making a door. Suggest the power tools that she should use to:
   a) cut the wood down to the right <u>thickness</u>
   b) make a <u>groove</u> for the handle to fit into

3) Calum wants to make a life-size cut-out of his favourite footballer. He's drawn their shape onto plywood. What power tool should he use to <u>cut it out</u>?

4) Give <u>two uses</u> of a <u>milling machine</u>.

5) John is using a lathe to make a snooker cue.
   a) Suggest one <u>safety check</u> he should carry out before using the machine.
   b) Describe how the material should be <u>held</u> in the machine.

Forming and Bending

You can often <u>change the shape</u> of a material by <u>folding</u> or <u>bending</u> it.

Sheet Metals Can be Folded

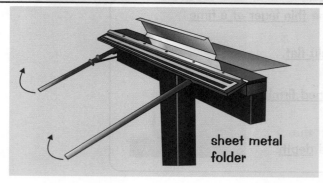

sheet metal folder

1) You can use a <u>sheet metal folder</u> to shape <u>sheet metals</u> such as aluminium and tin plate.
2) The outline of the product, e.g. a box, is marked out and cut from a <u>flat</u> sheet of metal.
3) You <u>feed the metal in</u> flat, make one fold then move the material through for the next fold.
4) Corners can then be <u>joined</u> using rivets, or by soldering, brazing, etc. — see page 51.

Most Metals Need to be Heated Before Bending

1) Some <u>thin</u> pieces of metal can be bent cold on a <u>jig</u> or <u>former</u>.
2) <u>Thicker</u> or harder metals have to be heated or <u>annealed</u> first (see page 29) and allowed to cool.
3) This makes them soft enough to bend easily, but the annealing process might have to be repeated as bending makes them go <u>hard</u> again — this is known as '<u>work hardening</u>'.

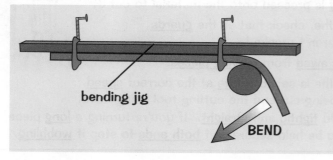

bending jig

BEND

Metal would have been heated and bent to make this shovel.

Iron and Steel are Forged

1) Metal, especially <u>iron</u> and <u>steel</u>, can be heated in a <u>forge</u>.

2) A forge is a fire with <u>air</u> blown into the middle of it to produce a very hot flame.

3) When the metal's hot enough to have softened sufficiently, it's taken out and <u>hammered into shape</u> on an <u>anvil</u>.

You need to bend your brain around this page...

<u>Different materials</u> are bent using <u>different methods</u>. Makes sense really — you wouldn't really want to try forging plastic, for example. You'd get a gooey puddle that wouldn't be much use for anything.

Forming and Bending

Wood and plastics can be bent and folded too.

Laminating _is_ Gluing Thin Strips _of Wood Together_

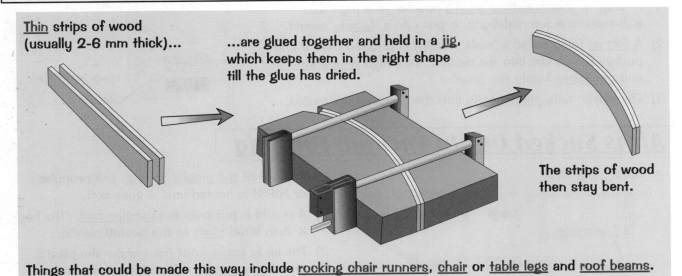

Thin strips of wood (usually 2-6 mm thick)...

...are glued together and held in a jig, which keeps them in the right shape till the glue has dried.

The strips of wood then stay bent.

Things that could be made this way include <u>rocking chair runners</u>, <u>chair</u> or <u>table legs</u> and <u>roof beams</u>.

Plastics _Can Also be_ Folded

1) <u>Line bending</u> is ideal for use with <u>acrylic sheets</u>, e.g. for making picture frames and pencil holders, etc.

2) It can be done manually or with a <u>line bender</u> or <u>strip heater</u>.

3) You rest the sheet on two bars and the element between them <u>heats</u> the plastic. You just need to position the sheet carefully, so that the line you want to bend along is <u>directly above</u> the element.

4) Once the plastic is <u>soft</u> it can be <u>bent</u>. When it <u>cools</u> it will stay in its <u>new shape</u>.

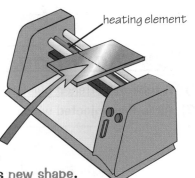

heating element

Practice Questions

1) What machine could you use to make this metal <u>magazine rack</u>?

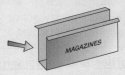

MAGAZINES

2) Sid wants to bend a <u>thick</u> piece of metal into the shape shown on the right.
   a) What does he need to do <u>before</u> he can bend the metal?
   b) <u>Sketch</u> a diagram to show how he can bend the metal using a <u>bending jig</u>.

3) What is an <u>anvil</u> used for?

4) a) Outline how <u>laminating</u> can be used to make bent wooden items.
   b) Suggest two products or components made by laminating wood.

5) Emma needs to <u>fold</u> a piece of <u>acrylic</u> for the picture frame she is making.
   a) Name a process she could use to fold the acrylic.
   b) Outline what happens during this process.

Casting and Moulding

There are plenty of ways to <u>mould</u> things — pressing, sucking and blowing just for starters.

Press Moulding *Shapes Thermosets*

1) A 'slug' of <u>thermosetting plastic</u> powder (see page 26), e.g. melamine formaldehyde, is put into a '<u>female</u>' mould.

2) A <u>former</u> (also called a 'male' mould) is pressed onto it and pushes the plastic into the mould. Very high <u>temperatures</u> and <u>pressures</u> liquify the powder.

3) The plastic sets <u>permanently</u> into the shape of the mould.

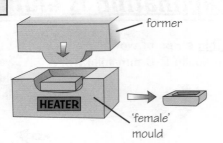

Air is Sucked Out In *Vacuum Forming*

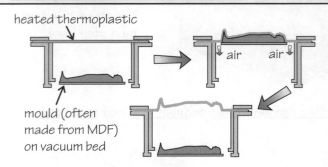

heated thermoplastic

mould (often made from MDF) on vacuum bed

air   air

1) A sheet of <u>thermoplastic</u> (e.g. polypropylene or HIPS) is heated until it goes soft.

2) A mould is put onto the <u>vacuum bed</u>. The bed is then lifted <u>close</u> to the heated plastic.

3) The air is <u>sucked</u> out from under the plastic, creating a <u>vacuum</u>. The air pressure from outside the mould then forces the plastic onto the mould.

Blow Moulding... Well... Blows Air In

1) A tube of <u>softened plastic</u> is inserted into a <u>solid mould</u>.

2) <u>Air</u> is then injected which forces the plastic to <u>expand</u> to the <u>shape</u> of the <u>mould</u>:

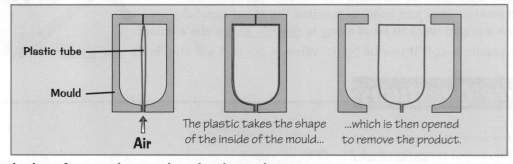

Plastic tube

Mould

Air

The plastic takes the shape of the inside of the mould...

...which is then opened to remove the product.

3) This method is often used to produce <u>bottles</u> and <u>containers</u>.

Die Casting *Also Uses a Mould*

1) Die casting is used to mould <u>metals</u> and <u>thermoplastics</u>.

2) The material is <u>melted</u> and poured into a <u>mould</u> (the 'die') which is in the shape of the product.

3) Some plastic resins can be <u>cold-poured</u> into moulds (without heating). They <u>harden</u> or <u>set</u> through a <u>chemical reaction</u>.

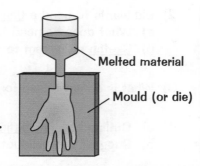

Melted material

Mould (or die)

Don't eat this book — because this page is all mouldy...

In both <u>vacuum forming</u> and <u>injection moulding</u> (next page) the moulds must have <u>rounded corners</u> and be slightly <u>tapered</u> (sloped) at the sides — so that the finished product can be <u>released</u> from the mould.

Casting and Moulding

Injection Moulding Uses Pressure to Mould Plastics

1) This is similar to casting, but the molten material is forced into a <u>closed mould</u> under <u>pressure</u>.
2) The moulds are often made from <u>tool steel</u> — it's very hard but it's also quite expensive.
3) The plastic is often melted using <u>built-in heaters</u>.
4) This is an industrial process which is usually <u>automatic</u>.
5) It can be used to make things like <u>plastic buckets</u> and <u>watering cans</u>.

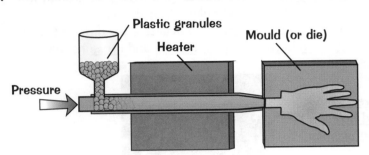

Plastics expert Brian had doubts about his new job.

Extrusion Produces Long, Continuous Strips

1) This process is very similar to injection moulding. It's used for some metals and thermoplastics.
2) The material is <u>melted</u> and forced under <u>pressure</u> through a <u>die</u>.
3) It produces long, <u>continuous</u> strips of the moulding exactly the same shape as the exit hole. It's used for products like <u>plastic-covered wire</u>, and <u>plastic and aluminium edgings</u>.

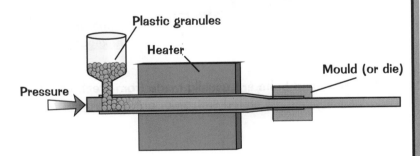

Practice Questions

1) a) What type of material is <u>press moulding</u> used to shape?
   b) Outline what happens during press moulding.

2) Describe the process of <u>vacuum forming</u>.

3) a) What moulding process is often used to make <u>plastic bottles</u>?
   b) Draw <u>diagrams</u> showing how this process could be used to make a plastic bottle.

4) a) What is a <u>die</u>?
   b) What types of materials can be moulded using <u>die casting</u>?

5) Peter is making a product using <u>injection moulding</u>.
   a) Suggest what type of material he is using.
   b) Outline the process of injection moulding.

6) Name two <u>products</u> that are made using <u>extrusion</u> moulding.

Fabricating

Screws and bolts are temporary ways of joining things together — you can take them apart if you need to.

Screws and Bolts are used with Wood, Metal and Plastic

There are different types of screws for use with wood, metals and plastics.

countersunk & slotted

round & slotted

cross

1) **Woodscrews** often require 'pilot' holes to be drilled before the screw is inserted. As the screw is turned by a screwdriver, the thread (the twisty bit around the outside of the screw) pulls it into the wood. Different types of head are available for different jobs, e.g. round, countersunk, slotted and cross heads.

2) **Self-tapping** screws have hardened threads and are designed to cut their own threaded holes in hard materials such as metals and hard plastics.

3) **Machine screws** have a straight shank and are used with washers and nuts. Heads vary (round, countersunk, etc.). Some are tightened with a screwdriver (cross and slotted types), and some with an Allen key (socket head).

head

thread   shank

4) **Bolts** are similar to machine screws but have a square or hexagonal head and are tightened with spanners.

5) Screws and bolts are usually made from steel, brass or stainless steel, and are 'self-finished' or plated with zinc, brass, chrome, or black japan (a black varnish).

Knock-Down Fittings are Non-Permanent Joints

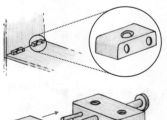

1) These are blocks, brackets (plastic or metal) and other fittings which enable furniture to be assembled and taken apart again easily.
2) They're used instead of traditional joints, and are very fast to use, but are nowhere near as strong as glued joints.
3) Most types are assembled with screwdrivers or Allen keys.
4) They're usually used for cheap 'flat-pack' furniture.

See pages 34-35 for more about knock-down fittings.

Well you could knock me down with a fitting...

Make sure you know all these bits and bobs, and what materials they join together. It'd be a shame to write screw when you meant bolt — even though they look a bit similar, you'll be chucking marks away.

Fabricating

Nails and rivets join things permanently — so you can't take them apart without damaging them.

Nails are Used for Joining Bits of Wood Together

1) These are similar in use to woodscrews but have a straight shank with no thread.

2) They're inserted with a hammer and can be punched below the surface with a nail punch to hide the head.

3) Nails are only used in wood and wooden products, e.g. plywood. They're much quicker to use than screws, but the joint they make is nowhere near as strong.

4) Nails are mostly made from steel, but special ones can be made from other metals, e.g. brass for use in boat building.

5) Like screws, nails come with a variety of head and shank shapes for different uses.

head

shank

Round wire nail

Rivets are Mainly Used for Joining Sheet Metal

1) A rivet is a metal peg with a head on one end. Rivets are mostly used for joining pieces of metal.

standard rivets

2) A hole is drilled through both pieces of metal and the rivet is inserted with a set (hammer-like tool). The head is held against the metal whilst the other end is flattened and shaped into another head with a hammer.

3) 'Pop' (or 'blind') rivets are now very common. They can be used where there is only access to one side of the material (hence 'blind' rivet). It's a fast and easy method of joining sheet metal.

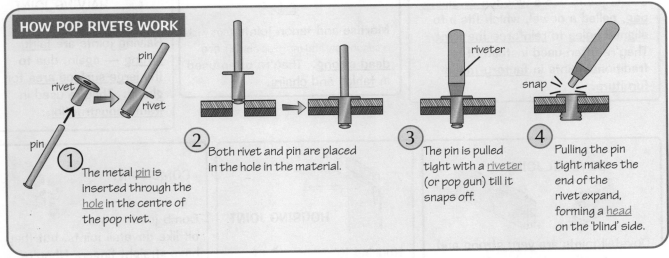

HOW POP RIVETS WORK

pin

rivet

rivet

pin

① The metal pin is inserted through the hole in the centre of the pop rivet.

② Both rivet and pin are placed in the hole in the material.

③ The pin is pulled tight with a riveter (or pop gun) till it snaps off.

riveter

④ Pulling the pin tight makes the end of the rivet expand, forming a head on the 'blind' side.

snap

Practice Questions

1) Jim is using screws to join the wood in his product together.
   a) What type of screws should Jim use?
   b) List three different kinds of screw head.

2) a) What are knock-down fittings?
   b) Give one advantage and one disadvantage of using knock-down fittings.
   c) Where are knock-down fittings often used?

3) Give one advantage and one disadvantage of using screws rather than nails.

Fabricating

Here are yet more ways of <u>fixing things together</u>...

Some <u>Joints</u> <u>are</u> Stronger than Others

EXAM TIP
Make sure you can say what the different types of joint are used for.

1) There are dozens of different <u>joints</u> for use in different situations. It's important to use the right joint in the right place.

2) Many joints <u>need</u> to be <u>glued</u> together. Some joints (e.g. dovetail joints) hold together without glue, but gluing makes them more <u>secure</u> and <u>permanent</u> (see the next page for more on glue).

BUTT JOINT

Pretty <u>weak</u> but very <u>quick</u> and <u>simple</u>. They're often used in <u>cheap pine furniture</u>.

MITRE JOINT

Mitre joints are <u>similar to butt joints</u> but prettier (they hide the end grain), <u>trickier to cut</u>, and have a slightly larger gluing area. They're used for <u>picture frames</u>.

REBATE JOINT

Rebate joints have a <u>larger surface area</u> for gluing than butt joints, so they're a <u>bit stronger</u>. They're used in some <u>drawers</u> and <u>boxes</u>.

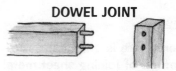

DOWEL JOINT

Dowel joints use a <u>wooden or plastic peg</u>, called a dowel, which fits into aligned <u>holes</u> to <u>reinforce the joint</u>. They're often used instead of traditional joints in <u>factory-made furniture</u>.

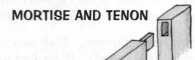

MORTISE AND TENON

Mortise and tenon joints (cut with a tenon saw and mortise chisel) **are <u>dead strong</u>**. They're often used in <u>tables</u> and <u>chairs</u>.

HALVING JOINT

Halving joints are <u>fairly strong</u> — again, due to the <u>large surface area</u> for gluing. They're used in <u>frame construction</u>.

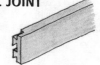

DOVETAIL JOINT

Dovetail joints are <u>very strong</u> and look <u>attractive</u>. They're often used in <u>drawer</u> construction. They're the <u>bee's knees</u>, but they're a <u>pain in the neck to make</u>. Unless you have a dovetail jig (see p. 52).

HOUSING JOINT

Housing joints are often used in shelving units — they provide a <u>good surface area</u> for gluing, and the shelf is supported from the front to the back.

COMB JOINT

Comb joints are a bit like dovetail joints, but they have <u>straight fingers</u> (they're sometimes called <u>finger joints</u>). They're a bit <u>easier</u> to make and are <u>strong</u> because of the <u>large contact area</u>. They're used for things like <u>boxes</u>.

I'm going to have a joint of lamb for my tea...

There's a fair bit to learn here — make sure you know the names of the different joints and what they're used for, then you can move on to adhesives, soldering, brazing and welding. Ooh, the excitement.

Fabricating

You Need to Choose the Right Adhesive for the Job

1) There are many different <u>types</u> of adhesive for use with different <u>materials</u> and for different jobs, e.g. <u>PVA</u> (for wood), <u>acrylic cement</u> (for plastics) and <u>contact adhesive</u> and <u>epoxy resin</u> (for lots of materials).

2) Adhesives will only work properly if you choose the <u>right one</u> for the job, and if the surfaces to be joined are really <u>clean</u>.

3) Some plastics <u>can't</u> be glued because they're too <u>smooth</u>, and have a <u>greasy</u> texture which stops the glue from '<u>keying in</u>'.

> You often get a little tube of PVA wood glue with flat-pack furniture to reinforce joints.

Soldering, Brazing and Welding are for Joining Metal

All these methods of joining metals need <u>heat</u>.

1) <u>Soldering</u> is a relatively <u>low temperature</u> process. Solder, made from <u>tin</u> and other metals, is melted onto the components to be joined — it sticks them together when it cools and solidifies. A <u>soldering iron</u> or a <u>blow torch</u> can be used for this process.

soldering iron

blow torch

2) <u>Brazing</u> is a <u>higher temperature</u> process which uses <u>brass spelter</u> as the joining material. It's much <u>stronger than soldering</u>. Either a <u>gas brazing torch</u>, a <u>blow torch</u>, or a brazing attachment for an <u>electric-arc welder</u> is used to heat the joint.

3) <u>Welding</u> is by far the <u>strongest</u> method of joining metal. It uses a <u>very high temperature</u> from an <u>oxyacetylene torch</u>, an <u>electric-arc welder</u> or a <u>laser</u> to actually <u>melt</u> the edges of the joint so that they flow together. Welding can also be used to fill in thinned metal or slight <u>gaps</u> — metal from a <u>welding rod</u> is melted on.

welding mask

— to protect your eyes from the bright light and UV radiation from the welding arc. It also protects your face from heat and sparks.

welding rod

Practice Questions

1) What is the disadvantage of using <u>butt joints</u>?

2) John is making a <u>wooden chair</u>.
   Suggest what type of joint he might use to join the legs to the seat.

3) Simon is making a plastic clock. He is using <u>adhesive</u> to join the components.
   a) What type of adhesive should he use?
   b) Why are some plastics <u>not suitable</u> for gluing?

Controlling Accuracy

Picture this — an evil twist of fate has left you to make 3000 identical ornamental pigs. <u>Accurately</u>. The idea of measuring out every pig fills you with dread. Fear not... it's <u>templates</u> and <u>jigs</u> to the rescue...

Templates _are Used to Make_ Repetitive Shapes

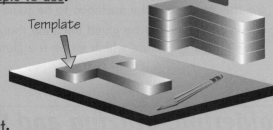
Template

1) <u>Templates</u> and <u>patterns</u> are very <u>easy to make</u> and <u>simple to use</u>.

2) You can use them to <u>reproduce</u> any number of <u>identical shapes</u> from one original <u>pattern</u> (template). The template is used to <u>draw</u>, <u>scribe</u> or <u>cut round</u>.

3) As long as your template is <u>accurate</u> the batch of components you make with it should <u>all</u> be <u>accurate</u> too — using a template makes the products <u>consistent</u>.

The boyband template — strong, hard-wearing and definitely used repetitively

4) <u>Templates</u> need to be <u>strong</u> and <u>hard-wearing</u> — so that they can be used <u>repetitively</u> without getting damaged or worn.

5) You can also <u>check</u> all your components against the template once you've cut them out.

Jigs _Help Manufacture_ Repetitive Components

1) A jig <u>guides</u> the <u>tools</u> that are working on a component, or holds the workpiece <u>in position</u> so you know that you're machining in the right place.

2) <u>Jigs</u> come in many <u>different shapes and sizes</u> and can be <u>specifically</u> made for a particular job.

3) They're designed to <u>speed up production</u> and <u>simplify</u> the <u>making</u> process.

4) Although jigs are really useful, they can take a <u>long time</u> to <u>make</u>. So it's not worthwhile using one if you're only going to make a few products.

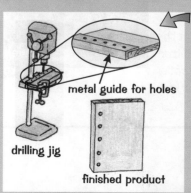

metal guide for holes

drilling jig

finished product

5) A <u>drilling jig</u> gets rid of the need for complex <u>marking out</u>. It can also help cut down on <u>errors</u>, and make sure that components are <u>consistent</u>.

6) Jigs can help with complex <u>cutting</u> jobs too. E.g. a <u>dovetail jig</u> enables complex joints (see p. 50) to be machined with a <u>router</u> very <u>quickly</u> and <u>easily</u>, and with <u>minimal measuring</u> and marking out.

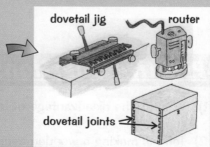

dovetail jig   router

dovetail joints

This revision malarkey is getting a bit repetitive...

In short, <u>templates</u> and <u>jigs</u> make life <u>easier</u>. Sadly, you'll need to write a bit more than that if they come up in the exam — handily though, all the <u>details</u> you need are on this page. Learn 'em.

Controlling Accuracy

Fixtures are Attached to Tools to Improve Accuracy

1) Fences are attached to <u>power</u> and <u>machine tools</u> to help <u>guide</u> either the tool or the material.

2) They can be set up to <u>repeat</u> the same action over and over again — ensuring <u>consistency</u> between the products in a batch.

3) There are different types of fixtures. For example:

Fences

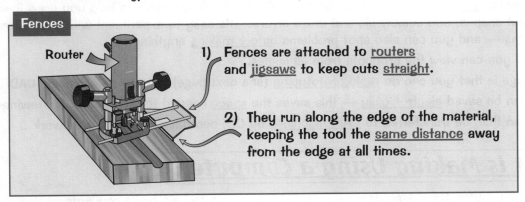

Router

1) Fences are attached to <u>routers</u> and <u>jigsaws</u> to keep cuts <u>straight</u>.

2) They run along the edge of the material, keeping the tool the <u>same distance</u> away from the edge at all times.

Mitre Fence

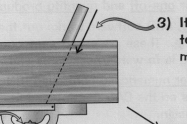

1) A mitre fence can be attached to machines like <u>sanders</u>, <u>band saws</u> and <u>circular saws</u> to help you cut or sand at an <u>angle</u>.

2) The fence has a <u>pivot</u> which can be set to the exact angle that you want to cut along.

3) It then <u>guides</u> the cutting tool towards the material...

4) ...so that it's cut at the right angle.

Practice Questions

1) What are <u>templates</u> used for?

2) a) Give <u>one advantage</u> of using a jig when making components.
   b) Adam is making a <u>one-off</u> product.
      Explain why using a jig won't save him time overall.

3) Martin is making a batch of chests of drawers. He needs to cut grooves along the side of each drawer using a router so they can be pulled in and out.
   a) Name a <u>fixture</u> that he could use to make sure these grooves are <u>straight</u>.
   b) Describe <u>how</u> this fixture will do its job.
   c) How will the fixture help Martin produce a batch of <u>identical products</u>?

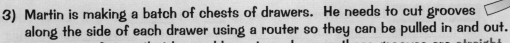

4) Holly is using a circular saw bench to cut a piece of wood at an angle of 55°.
   a) Name a <u>fixture</u> that she could use to help her cut the wood <u>accurately</u> at this angle.
   b) Describe <u>how</u> she would use this fixture.

Computerised Production

Here's a spot of <u>Computer Aided Design</u> and <u>Computer Aided Manufacture</u>, or CAD/CAM to its friends.

CAD is Designing Using a Computer...

1) <u>CAD</u> (Computer Aided Design) can be very useful when you're <u>developing</u> your ideas.
2) CAD software ranges from <u>2D drawing</u> programs (e.g. TechSoft 2D Design) to <u>3D modelling</u> packages (e.g. Pro/DESKTOP® or SolidWorks®).
3) CAD helps designers <u>model</u> and <u>change</u> their designs quickly. There are tools to help you draw lines, set angles, repeat shapes, add colour, fill, and erase errors. It's easy to experiment with alternative <u>colours</u> and <u>forms</u> — and you can also spot problems <u>before making</u> anything.
4) In 3D programs, you can view the products from <u>all angles</u>.
5) Another advantage is that you can do <u>rapid prototyping</u> (see next page) of your design using CAD/CAM.
6) CAD drawings can be saved <u>electronically</u> — this saves the <u>space</u> needed to store loads of drawings.
7) CAD drawings can then be transferred to <u>CAM machines</u> by CD, pen drive or across a network...

...and CAM is Making Using a Computer

1) <u>CAM</u> stands for Computer Aided Manufacture — using computers to help <u>make</u> products.
2) It's done by <u>computer-controlled machines</u> that convert designs produced using CAD into products for <u>one-off</u> and <u>quantity production</u> (see next page).
3) In these <u>CAD/CAM systems</u>, CAD software works out the coordinates of each point on the drawing. These are called <u>x,y,z coordinates</u> — x is the left/right position, y is forwards/backwards and z is up/down.
4) CAM machines are <u>computer numerically controlled (CNC)</u> — they can <u>follow</u> the x,y,z coordinates on the CAD drawing and move the tools to cut out or build up your design.
5) Some CAM machines are <u>2-axis</u> — they only use x and y coordinates so can only cut out <u>2D shapes</u>, e.g. laser cutters (see below) are used to make stencils. Others are <u>3-axis</u> machines — these use x, y, and z coordinates so they can cut out <u>3D shapes</u>.
6) <u>CNC lathes</u> and <u>machining centres</u> are both CAM machines. Other examples include:

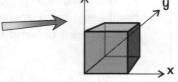

<u>Milling machines</u> Milling machines <u>remove</u> material from a larger piece of material to shape and create a product. They're <u>3-axis</u> machines so can cut out <u>3D shapes</u>.

tool head

<u>CNC routers</u> CNC routers are able to cut out <u>3D shapes</u> from a block of material using different sized cutting tools — they're <u>3-axis</u> machines. They can also be used to <u>engrave</u> things.

<u>Laser-cutters</u> Laser cutters are used to <u>cut</u> and <u>engrave</u> things. Laser-cutters on <u>high power settings</u> cut <u>right through</u> the material. <u>Lower power settings</u> are used for <u>engraving</u>. Laser-cutters can only be used on sheet materials — they're <u>2 axis</u> machines so they <u>can't</u> cut out 3D objects.

Learn this CAD/CAM stuff — or you'll look like a right tool...

<u>CAD</u> and <u>CAM</u> are all the rage in designing and making circles these days. Everybody's at it — not surprising considering how useful they are. Sadly, that means examiners really love <u>testing</u> you on it.

Computerised Production

CAD/CAM is Used to Make One-off Items...

1) Some machines are used to produce one-off items like <u>student project pieces</u>, <u>models</u> and <u>prototypes</u>.

2) For example, <u>3D printers</u> can be used for <u>rapid prototyping</u> — they convert your design from an image on screen into a <u>3D model</u>.

...And Large Quantities of A Product

1) Designs can be drawn <u>once</u> in CAD and then <u>copied and pasted</u> so that the CAM machine will cut out more than one shape from the material at a time. This is useful in <u>batch production</u>.

2) CAD/CAM can also be used to <u>mass-produce</u> complicated products. Each part can be manufactured by a <u>different machine</u> and the parts can be assembled quickly.

3) Products can be machined at <u>high speed</u>, and the machines can run <u>24 hours a day</u> — so loads of things can be manufactured in a <u>short time</u>.

4) CAM machines are really <u>accurate</u> — they make large numbers of <u>identical</u> products, ensuring <u>consistency</u> between products.

There are Different Types of Computer Software

It's not just CAD/CAM. You can use computer software to help with <u>all sorts</u> of tasks.

- <u>Graphics</u> programmes like Abode® Photoshop®, Adobe® Illustrator®, Serif DrawPlus™ and CorelDraw® are used for designing graphics for things like <u>packaging</u> and <u>posters</u>.

- <u>Database</u> software is used to <u>organise electronic information</u>, e.g. keep track of <u>stock</u> levels. You can get specialist database software (e.g. Microsoft® Access) or use <u>spreadsheet</u> software (such as Microsoft® Excel). Spreadsheets are useful for doing <u>calculations</u>, e.g. working out <u>costs</u>.

Word-processing programmes, e.g. Microsoft® Word are used to create text documents like letters and invoices.

Practice Questions

1) a) What does <u>CAD</u> stand for?
   b) Give an example of a piece of <u>3D CAD software</u>.
   c) Suggest why it might be a <u>good idea</u> to use <u>CAD</u> to design a product.

2) a) What is <u>CAM</u>?
   b) What is meant by CAM being '<u>computer numerically controlled</u>'?

3) Give an example of how CAM can be used to make <u>one-off</u> products.

4) Give <u>one advantage</u> of using CAD/CAM to make products in <u>large quantities</u>.

5) Suggest a piece of software that could be used to <u>organise</u> electronic information.

Social Responsibility

Manufacturers have a responsibility to make sure that their products are properly <u>labelled</u>. Information about <u>safety</u>, <u>product care</u> and <u>disposal</u> is often given using <u>signs and symbols</u>.

Labels Give Information About Product Safety...

1) Products may be labelled to show that they've met certain <u>standards for safety</u> or <u>quality</u>. These standards are set by different organisations, depending on the type of product.

The <u>British Standards Institution (BSI)</u> is one example. Products which meet their standards are awarded the Kitemark — manufacturers can put this on their label (many plastic products have it <u>moulded</u> on).

 Certain types of product must also meet <u>EU standards</u> for safety, shown by the '<u>CE</u>' mark, before they can be sold in Europe.

<u>Electrical goods</u> can be awarded safety marks by the <u>British Electrotechnical Approvals Board</u> (BEAB).

2) Labels might also include specific <u>safety warnings</u>, e.g.

"small parts may represent choking hazard"

EXAM TIP
You might be given a symbol and asked to explain its meaning — make sure you can.

...and Other Important Stuff

1) Labels sometimes give information about how to <u>look after</u> a product:

"store out of direct sunlight"

↑ **THIS WAY UP** ↑

"clean with mild detergent only"

FRAGILE

This symbol is often used on packaging for products that need to be transported with care.

2) Some products are labelled to show that they meet certain <u>environmental</u> or <u>ethical standards</u>. For example:

© 1996 FSC A.C.
FSC

The logo of the <u>Forest Stewardship Council (FSC)</u> shows that the <u>timber</u> in a product has come from a <u>sustainably managed</u> forest.

3) You can often find out how to <u>dispose</u> of a product or its packaging by looking at the label too:

This symbol shows that the <u>product</u> or <u>packaging</u> is <u>recyclable</u>...

(alu)
... this one means that the packaging is made from <u>recyclable aluminium</u>.

The Wheelie Bin symbol shows the product is <u>electrical</u> or <u>electronic equipment</u> and should be disposed of at a <u>suitable collection site</u>.

It's your responsibility to learn this stuff...

It's also <u>your responsibility</u> to take this lot into account when you're designing and making your own product. You'll get <u>more marks</u> and, more importantly, you'll be a better <u>human being</u>. Excellent.

Social Responsibility

When you're designing you should take into account the <u>needs</u> and <u>views</u> of a wide variety of people.

Products Need to be Accessible for Disabled Users

Lots of products are specifically designed to help people with <u>disabilities</u>.

1) Some packaging, e.g. for medicines, has <u>Braille</u> labelling to give blind people information.

2) Control buttons can be made brightly coloured and extra large, so they're easy to find and press. For example, telephones, TV remotes and calculators are made with very big buttons.

3) Products such as <u>timers</u> can be designed with <u>visible</u> signals as well as audible ones so that deaf people can be alerted.

Some people will find it easier to use a calculator with bigger buttons.

4) <u>Instructions</u> can be given in <u>picture</u> or <u>diagram</u> form so that people who have difficulty reading text can still use the product.

5) Designers also have to think about <u>wheelchair users</u>. For example, trains and buses need to be designed to have wheelchair access.

Designers Need to Think About Age Groups

People in different <u>age groups</u> have different <u>physical limitations</u>. For example:

You need to take <u>anthropometrics</u> into account for different age groups — see p. 8.

1) Small children and some elderly people may not be able to manipulate <u>small parts</u> and may have difficulty opening <u>packaging</u>...

2) ...or <u>holding</u> and <u>using</u> products — so designers may think about putting large, easy-to-grip handles on products like cutlery.

Not Everyone Sees a Product in the Same Way

1) You might think the <u>mobile phone</u> is the <u>best thing</u> since sliced bread — it makes it loads easier to stay in touch with your mates and you can always let your mum know when you'll be home for tea.

2) <u>Not everyone agrees</u> though. Some people get annoyed by loud phonecalls on trains.

3) When you design a product you need to think about <u>opposing viewpoints</u> like these — and try to make sure that your product has a mainly <u>positive</u> impact on society.

Practice Questions

1) a) What <u>symbol</u> would you see on a product that has been tested by the BSI and meets their standards?
   b) What does the <u>CE</u> symbol mean?
   c) What does the <u>FSC logo</u> show about a timber product?

2) Apart from safety and quality information, what else might you find on a <u>product label</u>?

3) How could a smoke alarm be designed so it's suitable for <u>deaf people</u>?

4) Frank is designing a tin opener.
   a) Suggest how he could make sure it's suitable for <u>infirm elderly people</u>.
   b) <u>Explain</u> your answer.

Legal and Moral Issues

Designers and manufacturers have <u>legal</u> responsibility to make sure their products don't <u>harm</u> people.

Products Must be Safe to Use

1) Think about whether people could hurt themselves while <u>using</u> the product.

2) Sometimes it's <u>impossible</u> to avoid potential harm <u>completely</u> (e.g. sharp tools), but for these products you should at least try to <u>minimise</u> the risks.

- Think whether the product could be dangerous if it's <u>misused</u>. You could put <u>instructions</u> and/or <u>safety warning</u> labels on the product to try and stop misuse.
- Make sure your design is <u>ergonomic</u> and won't cause <u>long-term health problems</u>. For example, a chair with a badly designed backrest could cause awful <u>backache</u> after long-term use.
- Products shouldn't have unnecessary <u>sharp corners</u> or <u>edges</u> for people to cut themselves on.
- <u>Toys</u> often end up in <u>children's mouths</u>, so don't finish the surface with a toxic paint or varnish. Check this out at the <u>research</u> stage and choose a <u>non-toxic</u> range of surface treatments.
- <u>Small components</u> must be firmly attached so that a child <u>can't</u> pull them off — this would be a <u>choking hazard</u>. They must be safely attached too — not using sharp metal spikes.
- Use <u>standard components</u> (e.g. knock-down fittings) where appropriate — these have already been <u>rigorously tested</u> by their manufacturer to make sure they're safe.

There Are Laws About Product Safety and Quality...

Manufacturers who produce <u>unsafe</u> or <u>unreliable</u> products are probably <u>breaking</u> one of these <u>laws</u>:

1) <u>Consumer Protection From Unfair Trading Regulations</u> ensure that any claims made about a product (e.g. that it is hard-wearing, long-lasting, waterproof) must be true.

2) <u>General Product Safety Regulations</u> state that nobody can put a product on the market unless it's safe.

3) <u>The Sale Of Goods Act</u> ensures that products perform as you would expect and that goods last a reasonable length of time.

4) <u>Fire Safety Regulations</u> cover upholstered furniture and cushions, etc. to ensure that they don't catch fire easily and don't give off really toxic fumes when they burn.

...and Standards for Safety and Quality...

1) Organisations like the <u>British Standards Institution</u> produce strict standards on product <u>safety</u> and <u>quality</u>. Companies which meet the BSI's standards are allowed to display their <u>Kitemark</u> (see p. 56).

2) It's <u>worthwhile</u> for a company to try to meet these standards, as it could make their products <u>more profitable</u> — many consumers are more willing to buy '<u>approved</u>' products, or will <u>pay more</u> for them.

Moral Issue 23 — Is it right to eat the last chocolate biscuit?

OK, so this stuff might not be the most thrilling part of resistant materials — but it is <u>dead important</u>, so make sure you <u>learn it</u>. You can have a chocolate biscuit when you're done. Just not the last one.

Legal and Moral Issues

Manufacturers also have <u>moral</u> and <u>legal</u> responsibilities to make sure that their <u>employees</u> have <u>fair working conditions</u> and a <u>safe</u> working environment.

Working Conditions Can Affect People, Costs and Sales

Manufacturers can <u>reduce costs</u> by:

1) Paying workers <u>less money</u>.
2) Increasing staff <u>working hours</u>.
3) Reducing <u>sick pay</u> and <u>holidays</u>.
4) Reducing the amount of money spent on <u>health and safety</u> (see p. 74-77).

Employees at this factory work in black and white to cut costs.

<u>BUT</u> if they did this, then:

1) They could <u>lose employees</u> — or employees could go on <u>strike</u>.
2) They could also <u>anger</u> potential <u>customers</u> — who might then choose <u>not</u> to buy the company's products.

None of this would be <u>good for business</u>.

There Are Initiatives for Better Working Conditions

The <u>Ethical Trading Initiative</u> (ETI) was set up to address concerns about products being made by <u>child labour</u> or in factories with <u>poor working conditions</u>, etc.

1) The ETI promotes <u>better conditions</u> for workers in <u>developing countries</u>.
2) It's a group of <u>companies</u>, <u>trade unions</u> and <u>volunteer groups</u> from all over the world.
3) Companies in the ETI agree to meet <u>standards</u> covering things like <u>wages</u>, <u>working hours</u> and <u>health and safety</u>.
4) The ETI <u>checks</u> that companies are following the rules and gives them <u>advice</u> about how they can improve.

Practice Questions

1) Name a product where it's impossible to completely prevent potential harm. Explain why.

2) Give <u>two ways</u> of making sure toys are as <u>safe</u> as possible for children.

3) Why is it a good idea to use <u>standard components</u> wherever possible?

4) Katie is designing a bed. She is assessing whether her product will break any <u>laws</u>.
Which laws cover the following things?
a) Whether the bed will last a long time.
b) Whether the mattress will give off toxic fumes if it catches fire.

5) Why is it <u>worthwhile</u> for a company to try and meet the strict safety standards produced by organisations like the BSI?

6) John runs a manufacturing business. He wants to reduce costs and decides to cut his employees' wages and increase their working hours.
<u>Why</u> might this be a <u>bad idea</u> for the business?

Cultural Issues

Important stuff this — you wouldn't want to go making a fool of yourself in the design stakes after all.

Culture is A Way of Life

1) The culture of a particular country or group of people covers everything from their religion, beliefs and laws to their language, food, dress, art and traditions. Phew.

2) If you're designing a product aimed at a specific target market, you'll have to take into account the views and feelings of people from that particular culture — that way you don't isolate or offend anybody.

3) If you want to sell your product globally, then you're going to have to take into account the views of as many different cultures as possible.

Culture can mean a lot of different things...

Cultural Differences Affect Designing

1) An example of a cultural difference is different ways of eating. Traditionally, Japanese people eat at a low table sitting on the floor.

2) If you were making a table for the Japanese market, you'd need to consider reflecting this tradition by making your table with shorter legs than a traditional European table has.

3) Culture can also affect aesthetics (looks). Some cultures are associated with particular patterns or colours, e.g. green is often associated with Islam and also with Ireland.

4) Many designers look to other cultures for design inspiration, e.g. minimalist design started in the US but was inspired by Dutch art and traditional Japanese architecture.

5) The geometric patterns in Islamic art have inspired many designers.

Cultural Issue 4 — Is it acceptable to own 5ive's greatest hits?

Answer: yes, but only if you can sing along to all the words. Again, this is all stuff you need to consider when designing and making your own product. Questions on this sort of thing could come up in the exam too.

Cultural Issues

Designers Must Be Aware of the Feelings of Others

Designers need to be <u>sensitive</u> to the feelings of different groups in society.

1) They need to make sure that designs do not <u>put off</u>, <u>insult</u> or <u>offend</u> people for <u>political</u>, <u>religious</u>, <u>gender</u> or <u>cultural</u> reasons.

2) Certain <u>symbols</u> will offend some people no matter how they're used, e.g. a swastika.

3) Other symbolism will offend people if they believe it's been <u>misused</u> or <u>abused</u>. This is especially true for religious symbols.

4) But it's not only abuse of religious symbols which can cause offence. Other <u>images</u>, <u>colours</u> and <u>styles</u> can easily put people from certain cultures off a product. For example, in China, <u>red</u> is seen as <u>good luck</u> and <u>black</u> is thought to bring <u>bad luck</u>.

Carol's Comics
— so simple, even a <u>woman</u> can understand them.

This sort of thing might have appeared in the 1920s...

...but you mightn't get away with it today.

5) <u>Sexism</u> and <u>racism</u>, either in text or in images, is sure to offend loads of people.

6) Some people are offended by images containing <u>nudity</u> and <u>violence</u>.

7) It's impossible to list <u>everything</u> that could cause <u>someone</u>, <u>somewhere</u> offence. Designers just have to try and put themselves in other people's shoes, and <u>imagine</u> how they might feel when they see the design.

Practice Questions

1) Name <u>three</u> things that are part of a country's <u>culture</u>.

2) Why do you have to take into account cultural views when designing a product for a <u>specific market</u>?

3) In some cultures, people like to eat together in <u>large family groups</u>. Explain how you'd take this into account if you were designing a <u>dining table</u>.

4) Give an example of a design that might <u>offend</u> people and explain why it would be offensive.

5) John is designing a set of <u>key fobs</u>.
   a) Sketch a design for a key fob that might appeal to a very <u>patriotic British person</u>.
   b) Explain why John might <u>avoid</u> using a <u>cross</u> on his designs.

6) Give one example of how a particular colour might <u>appeal</u> to people from a certain background.

Sustainability

Sustainable Products are Better for the Environment

Sustainability means not causing <u>permanent damage</u> to the environment and not using up <u>finite resources</u> (ones that'll run out eventually). How sustainable a product is depends on:

What <u>materials</u> are used to make it, for example:
- do they come from <u>renewable</u> resources (ones that can be replaced) — or finite ones?
- are they <u>recyclable</u> or <u>biodegradable</u> (this means they'll break down over time) — or will the used product permanently take up space in landfill?

<u>Wood</u> is a <u>renewable</u> resource because trees can be <u>replanted</u>.

The <u>processes</u> used to make the product, for example:
- does the process need lots of <u>energy</u>?
- does it create lots of <u>waste</u> or <u>pollution</u>?

<u>Oil</u> is a <u>finite</u> resource — it will eventually <u>run out</u>.

Sustainability also depends on the <u>design</u> itself — how long-lasting and efficient the product is.

You can use the <u>6 Rs</u> when you're designing to <u>reduce the impact</u> that products have on the <u>environment</u> and make the whole process more <u>sustainable</u>...

Remember to Use the 6 Rs

1) REPAIR

- It's better to <u>fix</u> things <u>instead</u> of <u>throwing</u> them away and replacing them as soon as they break.
- This means designing things so they're <u>easy to repair</u> — a simple design with easily accessible parts is best. Manufacturers can still make a profit by selling <u>replacement parts</u>.

  E.g. when a <u>bicycle chain</u> eventually <u>wears out</u>, you don't need to buy a whole new bike — you just replace the chain.

- Products that can be repaired include <u>cars</u>, <u>watches</u> and <u>household appliances</u> like washing machines.
- Many <u>cheap</u> products are not designed to be repairable, and it's often not worth repairing products — it's cheaper to buy a new one.

2) RECYCLE

- Recycling means <u>reprocessing</u> materials so they can be used again. (See page 65 for more on this.) It uses <u>less energy</u> than obtaining <u>new</u> materials, e.g. by extracting metal.
- Loads of stuff can be recycled, including <u>paper</u>, <u>glass</u>, <u>aluminium</u>, <u>steel</u> and some <u>plastics</u>.
- Recycled plastic can be used to make everything from <u>drainpipes</u> to <u>furniture</u> and <u>clothes</u>.

<u>Disassembly</u> is also part of recycling. Products can be taken to <u>pieces</u> and their parts recycled. E.g. metal from a car could be melted down and used to make other things. Disassembled parts can also be <u>reused</u> in other products (see the next page).

The 7th R — Revise...

The exam paper is called "<u>Sustainability</u> and technical aspects of designing and making", so the chance that you'll be asked about sustainability is pretty high. Best give these pages <u>plenty</u> of attention then...

Sustainability

3) REUSE

- Customers can <u>extend a product's life</u> by using it again, e.g. refillable <u>printer cartridges</u>.
- Some people <u>reuse</u> products for <u>other purposes</u>, e.g. using an <u>old car tyre</u> to make a swing.
- Reusing a product means you don't have to use up <u>more material</u> and <u>energy</u> making a replacement.

4) RETHINK

- You might be able to <u>make</u> the product <u>work</u> in a <u>different way</u>, e.g. a radio that you <u>wind up</u> instead of running off batteries.
- Or you might be able to make a product that uses much <u>less energy</u>, e.g. <u>energy-efficient</u> light bulbs instead of traditional ones.
- Or you could make a product with <u>many functions</u> — for example, a mobile phone with an alarm clock and a camera is <u>three</u> products in <u>one</u>. This saves on <u>resources</u>, <u>manufacturing processes</u> and <u>disposal</u>.

5) REDUCE

- Some products have what's known as '<u>built-in obsolescence</u>'. This is when manufacturers design their product to <u>need replacing</u> within months or a few years, e.g. <u>mobile phones</u> and <u>MP3 players</u>.
- Making <u>long-lasting</u>, <u>durable</u> products instead <u>reduces</u> the <u>number</u> of products customers need to buy. Manufacturers would then be making fewer products and so <u>cutting down</u> on <u>energy</u> use, <u>transport</u> and <u>materials</u>.
- Designers can also try to use <u>less material</u> in making their product. For example, you could design the nets to make packaging so that very little material is <u>wasted</u> when they're cut out.

6) REFUSE

- You can <u>refuse</u> to buy a product if you think it's <u>wasteful</u> — e.g. it might use a lot of <u>unnecessary packaging</u> or be <u>inefficient</u> to run.
- When you're <u>designing</u> a product you can refuse to <u>use</u> materials that haven't been or can't be <u>recycled</u> or that are <u>harmful</u> to the environment.

"Sorry Santa, I just can't accept — there's far too much unnecessary packaging."

Practice Questions

1) a) What does the term <u>renewable resource</u> mean?
   b) What does the term <u>finite resource</u> mean?

2) Julie is designing a children's toy truck.
   Suggest some features that would make it <u>easy to repair</u>.

3) Name <u>three</u> materials that can be recycled.

4) How is recycling <u>different</u> from reusing?

5) a) What is meant by <u>built-in obsolescence</u>?
   b) Why is built-in obsolescence usually <u>bad</u> for the <u>environment</u>?

6) Bob is designing some disposable plastic cutlery.
   Suggest how he could use the <u>6 Rs</u> to reduce the cutlery's impact on the environment.

Sustainability

Yep, more on sustainability I'm afraid — there's a lot to cover on this topic...

Most Products Have a Limited Lifetime

1) Some products aren't <u>designed to last</u> for very long, e.g. <u>disposable razors</u> and <u>paper cups</u>.

2) <u>Phones</u>, <u>cameras</u> and <u>music players</u> are also examples of products that aren't really designed to last — manufacturers are constantly <u>replacing</u> them with newer, more <u>up-to-date</u> versions.

3) And <u>no</u> product will last <u>forever</u>. When a product reaches the <u>end</u> of its life, it has to be <u>disposed of</u>. Usually, another product has to be made to <u>replace it</u> too.

4) Because of this, it's important to make products using <u>renewable</u> materials — or, if that's not possible, from material that <u>has been</u> or <u>can be recycled</u>.

5) '<u>Design for Disassembly</u>' means designing products so that they can be <u>easily taken apart</u> at the end of their lifetime — this allows the <u>parts</u> and <u>materials</u> to be <u>reused</u> or <u>recycled</u> to make new products. Soon all <u>electronic</u> and <u>electrical goods</u> will have to be made this way.

Carry Out a Life Cycle Analysis

It's sometimes called a Life Cycle <u>Assessment</u>.

A <u>life cycle analysis (LCA)</u> looks at each <u>stage</u> of the <u>life</u> of a product — from the raw materials to when it's disposed of. It works out the potential <u>environmental impact</u>:

Choice of material

1) <u>Hardwoods</u> are often obtained from natural <u>rainforests</u>. Felling the trees destroys the habitat of pretty much everything living there (including people). <u>Softwoods</u> are a <u>greener choice</u>. They're usually from <u>managed plantations</u> — so more trees are planted and grow quickly to replace them. <u>Recycled</u> wood is also a good choice for the environment.

2) <u>Metals</u> have to be <u>mined</u> and <u>extracted</u> from their ores. Most <u>plastics</u> are made using <u>crude oil</u>, which is a <u>finite resource</u>. These processes need a lot of <u>energy</u> and cause a lot of <u>pollution</u>.

Some products can be <u>recycled</u> — the materials can be used again in new products.

Manufacture

1) <u>Manufacturing</u> products uses a lot of <u>energy</u> and other resources. It can also cause a lot of <u>pollution</u>.

2) You also need to think about <u>waste</u> material and how to <u>dispose</u> of it.

Using the product

<u>Using</u> the product can also damage the environment. E.g. <u>electrical products</u> use electricity generated by burning <u>fossil fuels</u>, and <u>paint</u> can give off <u>toxic fumes</u>.

Product Disposal

1) Products are often <u>disposed</u> of in a <u>landfill</u> site at the end of their life.

2) This takes up space and <u>pollutes</u> land and water (e.g. when paint washes off a product and gets into rivers).

Recycling — what a load of rubbish...

You should be able to carry out a <u>life cycle analysis</u> on a product — and show that you've <u>thought carefully</u> about the <u>impact</u> everything from its materials to its disposal will have on the <u>environment</u>.

Sustainability

Part of designing and making a product should involve thinking about how to <u>get rid of it</u>.

Throwing Away *Old Products Causes* Pollution

1) There are <u>laws</u> about what can be dumped into landfill sites — and what has to be <u>recycled</u> or <u>specially treated</u> to make it <u>safe</u>. That's because some chemicals used in products cause <u>serious problems</u> when they get into watercourses or into the soil.

Batteries have to be carefully disposed of because of the chemicals they contain.

2) Many materials can be recycled. Recycling can be either <u>primary</u>, <u>secondary</u> or <u>tertiary</u>:

Primary recycling is making the <u>same thing</u>.

e.g. a drinks can...

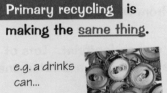

...gets melted down and made into ...

...<u>another</u> drinks can

Secondary recycling is making a <u>different thing</u>.

e.g. a HDPE drinks bottle...

...gets melted down and made into...

...a HDPE toy

Tertiary recycling is breaking something down to its <u>raw materials</u>.

e.g. a PET drinks bottle...

...is broken down <u>chemically</u>...

...and used as fuel or to make more plastic.

3) <u>Packaging</u> contributes to the problem of waste. Designers need to work out <u>how much</u> packaging is actually <u>needed</u> for a product, and how it can be safely <u>disposed of</u> or <u>recycled</u>.

Practice Questions

1) Give <u>two</u> examples of products that <u>aren't</u> designed to last.

2) What is meant by the term '<u>Design for Disassembly</u>'?

3) a) What is a <u>life cycle analysis</u>?
   b) What are the <u>four stages</u> of a life cycle analysis?

4) Ben is making a bench.
   In terms of the <u>environmental impact</u>, explain why:
   a) It would be better to make the bench out of <u>wood</u> than <u>metal</u>.
   b) It would be better to use a <u>softwood</u> than a <u>hardwood</u>.

5) Give <u>two factors</u> that should be considered during the design process in order to minimise problems with <u>product disposal</u>.

Environmental Issues

Just when you thought we'd covered <u>everything</u> there was to say about the <u>environment</u>...

Products have a *Carbon Footprint*

1) A <u>carbon footprint</u> is the amount of <u>greenhouse gases</u> (carbon dioxide, methane and other gases) released by doing or making something.

> Greenhouse gases are gases that contribute to the <u>greenhouse effect</u>. They limit how much heat can escape from the Earth's atmosphere — releasing lots of these gases is causing the planet's <u>temperature</u> to <u>rise</u>.

2) <u>All</u> products have a carbon footprint — because <u>carbon dioxide</u> is released when they're <u>made</u>, <u>transported</u> and <u>used</u>. That's because <u>fossil fuels</u> are burned to provide the <u>energy</u> for these processes, and this emits carbon dioxide.

3) So the more <u>energy</u> that's needed to make something, the <u>bigger</u> its carbon footprint.

4) <u>A lot</u> of <u>energy</u> is used to <u>manufacture plastics</u>, so plastic products have a <u>huge</u> carbon footprint.

5) A product's carbon footprint is also affected by the distance it travels from where it's <u>made</u> to where it's <u>used</u> (this is called <u>product miles</u>).

6) Making products so that they <u>use energy efficiently</u> could <u>reduce</u> their carbon footprint. Lots of appliances now have efficiency ratings, e.g. an A-rated fridge is more efficient than a D-rated one.

Carbon *Emissions Can Be* Traded *or* Offset

Some companies are trying to reduce the <u>impact</u> they have on the environment. Managing their <u>carbon footprint</u> is an important factor.

CARBON TRADING

1) The EU has put a <u>limit</u> on the <u>total amount</u> of <u>carbon dioxide</u> that power stations and big manufacturers can produce.

2) These companies get given <u>credits</u> which allow them to emit a <u>certain amount</u> of carbon dioxide.

3) Companies are allowed to <u>trade</u> credits with each other — the scheme means manufacturers who <u>pollute</u> have to <u>pay</u> to do so, while '<u>greener</u>' companies can <u>benefit financially</u>.

CARBON OFFSETTING

1) Some companies, like retailers, <u>don't</u> have to take part in carbon trading schemes because they don't pollute much.

2) They can <u>choose</u> to have any carbon emissions they do make <u>offset</u> though. This is often a <u>good marketing tool</u>.

3) Offsetting means <u>donating money</u> to projects that <u>reduce</u> carbon emissions — to <u>balance out</u> the greenhouse gases the company is responsible for.

4) Projects include <u>planting trees</u>, investing in <u>wind and solar power</u>, and <u>recycling projects</u>.

I have an issue with my environment — it's raining...

In the last few years, consumers have become far more <u>aware</u> of issues like these. As a result, many <u>manufacturers</u> have started to clean up their act and have tried to <u>reduce</u> their <u>environmental impact</u>.

Environmental Issues

Chemicals Can Harm the Environment

The processes used to make many everyday products often use or produce <u>harmful chemicals</u>...

DIOXINS

1) <u>Dioxins</u> are chemicals formed in production methods that use <u>chlorine</u> — these include the manufacture of <u>PVC</u> and the <u>bleaching</u> of wood pulp to make <u>paper</u> and <u>card</u>.

2) Dioxins get into the air, soil and water sources and <u>build up</u> in the <u>food-chain</u>. At high concentrations they can poison <u>humans</u> and <u>wildlife</u>.

3) <u>Emissions</u> of dioxins from manufacturing processes are now <u>tightly controlled</u>.

VOCs

1) <u>VOCs</u> (volatile organic compounds) are gases given off by a lot of <u>paints</u>, <u>varnishes</u> and <u>cleaning products</u>.

2) VOCs are major <u>air pollutants</u>, but they can also get into soil and water. Some are <u>greenhouse gases</u> and many are <u>toxic</u>.

3) Products with fewer VOCs are becoming available, e.g. '<u>low VOC</u>' or '<u>VOC-free</u>' paint.

CFCs

1) <u>CFCs</u> are gases that used to be used to keep <u>fridges cold</u> and as a <u>propellant</u> in <u>aerosols</u>.

2) When CFCs get into the <u>upper atmosphere</u> they break down the <u>ozone layer</u>. This is bad news because the ozone layer protects the Earth from the Sun's harmful UV radiation.

3) Using a lot of CFCs was making a '<u>hole</u>' in the ozone layer and letting through more UV radiation.

4) The use of CFCs has now been <u>reduced</u> — very <u>few aerosols</u> have them in today.

Practice Questions

1) a) What is a <u>carbon footprint</u>?
   b) Explain why <u>all products</u> have a carbon footprint.
   c) Suggest <u>one</u> way in which a product's carbon footprint might be <u>reduced</u>.

2) Describe what is meant by <u>carbon trading</u>.

3) Briefly describe how a company might <u>offset</u> their carbon emissions.

4) Why are <u>CFCs</u> bad for the environment?

5) Sarah is making a desk. She chooses <u>VOC-free</u> paint to finish it with. Why is this better for the <u>environment</u> than if she had chosen ordinary paint?

Production Methods

Small scale production means making a few of something. Large scale production could mean making millions. Different scales of production need different ways of organising things.

Jobbing Production is Making a One-off Product

1) This is where you make "one-of-a-kind" products. Every item will be different, to meet a customer's exact requirements.

2) This type of production is very labour intensive — it takes a lot of time to make each product. The workforce also needs to be highly skilled. So it's an expensive way to make things.

3) One-off production is used for all sorts of things, from made-to-measure furniture to buildings.

4) Prototypes for a new product are normally one-off products. If the prototype works well, the product might then be manufactured in greater volumes...

In school projects you usually make one-off products.

Batch Production is Making a Set Number of Products

1) This is where you make a specific quantity of a product — called a batch. E.g. you might make a batch of 10 racing car nose cones, or 2000 circuit boards for burglar alarms. Batches can be repeated as many times as necessary.

2) You do one process (e.g. cutting out) on the whole batch, then do another process (e.g. painting the parts you cut out). So it's quicker than making one-off products over and over again.

3) Batch production is used to manufacture a load of one product (sofas, say) — then a load of something a bit different (armchairs, for example).

4) The machinery and labour need to be flexible, so they can quickly change from making one batch to making another batch of a similar product.

5) The time between batches, when machines and tools may have to be set up differently or changed, is called down time. This wastes money — because you're not making anything to sell.

6) Batch production could also mean you get a backlog of half-made products, waiting for the slowest process (e.g. paint drying). So it's not as efficient as mass production (see the next page).

Trevor could only hope that his colleagues hadn't used the last of the milk.

Der der der der, derder-der der der — it's batch of the day...

In your exam, you might be given an example of a product and asked what method you would use to manufacture it. Avoid exam pain — learn these methods, and the amount of products they make.

Production Methods

Mass Production *is* Making Loads *of the* Same Product

1) Mass production is a high-volume production method — when you make <u>thousands</u> and <u>thousands</u> of <u>identical products</u>, like <u>cars</u> and <u>televisions</u>. You'd only do this for a <u>mass-market product</u> — where loads of people want to buy the same thing.

2) The different stages of production and manufacture are <u>broken down</u> into simple <u>repetitive tasks</u> which people can easily learn. Production often happens on an <u>assembly line</u> — the product moves further down the line for each different stage. Each worker only does a <u>small part</u> of the process.

3) Mass production often uses computer-aided manufacturing and <u>expensive specialised equipment</u>. E.g. you might use <u>vacuum-forming</u> to mould plastic in <u>jobbing</u> or <u>batch production</u>, but <u>injection moulding</u> is better for <u>mass production</u> — although it costs a lot to set up, it's much faster (see p.47).

4) <u>Recruitment</u> is relatively <u>easy</u> — most of your staff don't need to be highly skilled.

Continuous Production *is* Making Stuff Non-Stop

1) Continuous production is <u>highly automated</u>. It uses <u>expensive machines</u> that <u>run all the time</u>, without interruption, 24 hours a day.

2) That's because it would be too <u>expensive</u> to keep <u>stopping and restarting</u> the process, especially if certain conditions need to be kept <u>constant</u>, e.g. a high temperature in steel production.

3) The equipment is built to make <u>huge amounts</u> of only <u>one thing</u>, so it can be designed to be <u>very efficient</u>. It's great for making bulk amounts of materials — like steel, sheet glass, or synthetic fibres for cloth or rope.

Practice Questions

1) List the <u>four</u> main <u>production methods</u> in order of scale (from the smallest to largest scale).

2) Why are <u>one-off</u> products usually expensive to buy?

3) a) What type of production would you use to make a <u>specific quantity</u> of a product?
   b) Why, in that production method, do your workers and machinery need to be <u>flexible</u>?

4) What is '<u>down time</u>'? Why does it reduce efficiency?

5) A company is going to make <u>75 000</u> musical microwave ovens.
   a) What <u>method</u> of production will be best suited to this task?
   b) What is the <u>advantage</u> of this method when it comes to <u>hiring</u> workers?

6) Fred works in a factory that <u>mass-produces</u> cars. Fred only knows how to do the spray painting. Explain why the factory boss doesn't mind that Fred doesn't understand the rest of the process.

7) a) Why is continuous production very efficient?
   b) So why <u>isn't</u> continuous production used to make <u>everything</u>?

Quality Control

It's important that products are of a <u>satisfactory quality</u> — otherwise nobody will buy them.

Good <u>Design</u> and Good <u>Manufacture</u> <u>are</u> <u>Different</u>

A high-quality product should be well-designed <u>and</u> well-manufactured...

> **A well-designed product:**
> - can carry out its <u>function</u> really well
> - <u>looks</u> good and attracts consumers

> **A well-manufactured product:**
> - has been <u>made</u> to a <u>good standard</u> — things like the finish, folds, colour and material are all satisfactory
> - is <u>accurate</u> to the original design

<u>Quality</u> is Affected by <u>Materials</u> and <u>Processes</u>

The quality of your finished product will be affected by the <u>design choices</u> you make.

1) You need to choose the right <u>materials</u>. For example, aluminium would be a good choice of material to make a bicycle frame because it's light, strong and won't rust.
   (Steel would be a poorer choice because it'd make the bike <u>heavy</u> and likely to <u>rust</u>.)

2) You need to choose the right <u>processes</u>. For example, welding would be a good process for making the joints of a bike frame. (Soldering wouldn't be strong enough.)

<u>Quality Control</u> Checks the <u>Quality of Manufacture</u>

1) To make sure products are manufactured to a high quality, <u>quality control checks</u> must be included throughout the manufacturing process.

2) Quality control involves <u>testing samples</u> of components to check that they meet the manufacturer's specification. For example, they must be the right <u>colour</u> or the right <u>size</u>.

3) It's important the dimensions of components are <u>accurate</u>. If they aren't, the parts won't <u>fit together</u> properly when the product is assembled. To make sure that parts are the correct size they must be <u>measured accurately</u>.

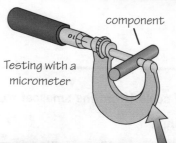

component

Testing with a micrometer

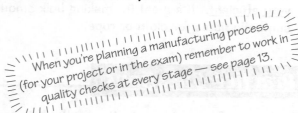

When you're planning a manufacturing process (for your project or in the exam) remember to work in quality checks at every stage — see page 13.

> - When components are checked for size they must be within a specific <u>tolerance</u>.
> - Tolerance is given as an upper (+) and lower (−) limit for the measurement.
> - For example, if a component should have a diameter of 20 mm (±0.5), then a <u>micrometer reading</u> of <u>19.9 mm</u> would be <u>OK</u> but <u>20.7 mm</u> would <u>not</u>.
> - Tolerances should be included on <u>working drawings</u>, to show the <u>limits</u> within which the product should be manufactured.

I can assure you that this page is quality...

A <u>high quality</u> product is one that <u>does its job</u> well, meets the <u>standards</u> set down by any relevant institutions, and is manufactured <u>consistently</u>. If it does all that, it ought to <u>keep customers happy</u> too.

Quality Control

There are Different Kinds of Testing

Failures at testing can <u>identify faults</u> with machining and tool settings and <u>eliminate costly waste</u>. Once you've spotted a <u>problem</u> you can <u>put it right</u>.

1) Measuring components with a micrometer is a time-consuming (and therefore costly) business. The process can be speeded up using <u>limit gauges</u>. These are usually double-ended, one end being machined to the <u>lower limit</u> and the other end to the <u>upper limit</u>.

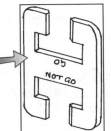

If the component fits through the upper limit but not the lower one, it's within the <u>acceptable range</u>.

EXAM TIP
In the exam you might be asked to suggest some quality control checks for a production process.

2) <u>Visual checks</u> are carried out to make sure that things like the <u>surface finish</u> and <u>overall appearance</u> of a product are up to scratch. Visual tests might also include using X-rays to spot defects, e.g. cracks in a welded joint. This is <u>non-destructive testing</u>.

Tom's destructive testing went a bit too far.

3) Some testing is <u>physical</u> and <u>destroys</u> the product to see <u>when</u> and <u>how</u> it fails. This is <u>destructive testing</u>. It helps manufacturers to write <u>safety instructions</u> for their products — e.g. how heavy a load the product can take.

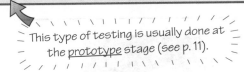
This type of testing is usually done at the <u>prototype</u> stage (see p. 11).

Practice Questions

1) What is <u>quality control</u>?

2) A part that should measure <u>21 mm</u> could actually be up to <u>3 mm</u> longer or shorter. How would this tolerance be written?

3) Sally is making a picture frame. The frame must have a thickness of **25 mm (±0.4)**. Would the following measurements be acceptable for this component?
   a) **25.2 mm**
   b) **25.5 mm**
   c) **24.8 mm**
   d) **24.5 mm**

4) Explain the advantage of using <u>limit gauges</u> rather than micrometers to measure components.

5) Pierre has made an Eiffel-Tower-themed table from <u>steel</u>. He is testing the table.
   a) Suggest an easy way to check whether the <u>edges</u> of the table top are smooth.
   b) What might be checked using <u>X-rays</u>?
   c) Pierre's boss thinks he should do a <u>destructive test</u> of the table's strength. <u>Describe</u> how Pierre might do this destructive testing.
   d) What would be the point of doing this destructive test?

New Technologies

Yep, I know there's been some stuff about CAD/CAM already. This page goes into a bit more detail about how CAM processes work, and some advantages and disadvantages of using CAD/CAM in industry.

CAM Processes can be Subtractive...

SUBTRACTIVE processes are when material is removed from a larger piece of material to create a product.

Examples of subtractive CAM systems are CNC routers, lathes, milling machines and laser cutting machines (see p. 54).

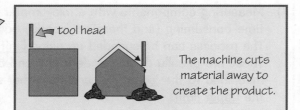

tool head

The machine cuts material away to create the product.

...or Additive

ADDITIVE processes work by adding material to build up the product rather than by removing it.

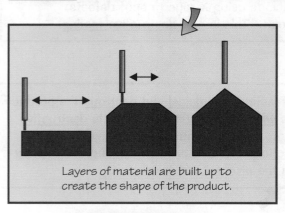

Layers of material are built up to create the shape of the product.

1) **3D Printing** works by printing layers of molten plastic, powder or wax on top of each other until the full 3D shape has been formed.

2) **Laminating** is when layers of paper, plastic or metal are cut with knives or lasers and stacked on top of each other to build a 3D model.

3) **Stereolithography** uses a laser beam to 'cure' liquid resin (turn it into a solid) in thin layers. This process is pricier and slower than 3D printing but more accurate.

4) **Laser-sintering** is similar to stereolithography but the laser fuses powder together instead of curing a liquid. It's quicker than stereolithography but the finish isn't quite so good.

Colin's attempts to build a 3D printer out of a typewriter, a sewing machine, an old bike and some string weren't going well.

Additive processes are used in rapid prototyping and rapid manufacture:
1) Rapid prototyping (converting a CAD drawing to a 3D model) is often done by 3D printing.
2) Rapid manufacture means using an additive process (often stereolithography) to make products or components instead of using a traditional process like moulding. At the moment rapid manufacture isn't widely used — but this could change as the technology develops.

Subtractive CAM — more useful than subtractive camels...

Now you're dead clear on what CAD and CAM are, you can get your head round the different processes they involve. And don't forget about rapid prototyping — it saves manufacturers loads of time.

New Technologies

New technologies can be brilliant. But, as with everything, there are some <u>disadvantages</u> too.

CAD/CAM has Lots of Benefits and a Few Drawbacks

It's very <u>expensive</u> to <u>buy</u> and <u>set up</u> CAD/CAM systems, but they <u>save money</u> in the <u>long run</u>. CAD/CAM has lots of benefits for designers and manufacturers in many different <u>industries</u>. For example:

 Products can be machined at <u>high speed</u>, and the machines can run <u>24 hours a day</u> — so loads of things can be manufactured in a <u>short time</u>. Machines can also work in conditions that would be <u>hazardous</u> to people, e.g. paint spraying.

 <u>Labour costs</u> are <u>lower</u> — <u>machines</u> are doing almost all the work.

 You can mass-produce <u>complicated products</u>. Each part can be manufactured by a <u>different machine</u> and the parts can be assembled quickly.

 CAM gives a <u>high quality</u> and more <u>reliable</u> finish — there's less potential for human error.

But...

 Computers can be affected by <u>software problems</u>, <u>viruses</u>, and <u>corrupted files</u> — potentially <u>slowing down</u> production.

 Because <u>fewer workers</u> are needed, <u>unemployment</u> might increase and <u>traditional skills</u> could be lost.

Globalisation — Buying and Selling Across the Globe

1) Nowadays it's a lot <u>easier</u> to <u>work with people</u> around the world, and to <u>transport goods</u>.

2) This is because of improvements in <u>communication technology</u> (phones and computers), <u>CAD/CAM</u> and <u>faster transport</u>. This has affected manufacturing in <u>two</u> main ways:

SAVINGS ON SHIPPING COSTS

<u>Designs</u> for products (e.g. cars) can be sent <u>electronically</u>...

...to be manufactured at a factory on the other side of the world, <u>near</u> where they'll be <u>sold</u>.

This means companies can <u>save</u> on the <u>costs</u> of <u>shipping</u> the finished products.

SAVINGS ON LABOUR COSTS

Some companies <u>design</u> their products in one country...

...have them <u>manufactured</u> in another (where labour is cheaper)...

...and then <u>ship</u> them back to wherever they'll be <u>sold</u>.

Practice Questions

1) a) What is the difference between an <u>additive</u> process and a <u>subtractive</u> process?
   b) Give two examples of subtractive CAM systems.
   c) Give two examples of additive CAM systems.

2) Explain what is meant by
   a) rapid prototyping   b) rapid manufacturing

3) Explain three <u>benefits</u> of using CAD/CAM in the design and manufacture of products.

4) Explain one <u>drawback</u> of using CAD/CAM in the design and manufacture of products.

5) Outline <u>two</u> factors that have contributed to <u>globalisation</u>.

6) Explain <u>two ways</u> in which globalisation can make products cheaper.

Health and Safety

Safety is essential when you make a product — you don't want to lose vital body parts.

Wear the Right Clothing and Protective Equipment

You should always wear appropriate protective clothing (called Personal Protective Equipment — PPE). It's the responsibility of your employer (or school) to provide and maintain this equipment.

If you're working with hazardous materials wear a face mask or goggles and strong protective gloves. If there are fumes make sure there's enough ventilation.

(A spray booth can be used to help remove fumes when using spray glue or paint.)

If the material is hot, you need to wear protective gloves and an apron. For some jobs (e.g. welding metal) you should also wear a face shield.

If you're making a lot of dust you should wear goggles and a face mask and check ventilation.

(Machines a bit like vacuum cleaners can be used to extract dust from the working area.)

When making large metal castings, you should wear a thick all-body suit, a face shield, gauntlets (thick gloves) and spats (to protect legs and feet).

Be Careful with Tools and Machinery...

1) The Health and Safety at Work Act (1974) was passed to make sure employers provide a safe working environment, and that they use safety signs to help reduce the risk of accidents.

2) When you're working with tools and machinery, make sure you have your sleeves rolled back, ties tucked in or taken off, apron strings tucked in and long hair tied back. Make sure there aren't any tripping hazards in the workshop. Clear up any spillages straight away.

3) By law, employers and workers must always use safe working practices for tools and machinery.

E.g. the pillar drill...

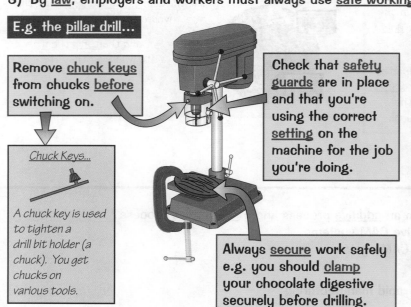

Remove chuck keys from chucks before switching on.

Chuck Keys...

A chuck key is used to tighten a drill bit holder (a chuck). You get chucks on various tools.

Check that safety guards are in place and that you're using the correct setting on the machine for the job you're doing.

Always secure work safely e.g. you should clamp your chocolate digestive securely before drilling.

Other health and safety procedures

1) Never leave any machines unattended while switched on.

2) Know how to switch off and isolate machines in an emergency.

3) Ensure that any dust and fume extraction equipment is working properly.

4) Never adjust a machine until you've switched it off and isolated it from the mains first.

5) Make sure nobody will distract you or knock you when you're working on the machine.

Watch where you point that tool — nearly had my eye out...

This page is all about minimising risks. Think about clothing, machinery and how to handle materials safely. It's all stuff that comes up when you write a risk assessment (see page 77...).

Health and Safety

...and Handle Materials and Waste Sensibly

1) Choose your materials sensibly — only use hazardous materials where absolutely necessary.
2) Make sure materials are safe to handle. For example, deburr metal (file down any rough edges) before you start work.
3) Be careful when you move long lengths of metal and timber, as it's a possible hazard to others.
4) Beware of naked flames or red-hot heating elements — and keep them away from flammable liquids.
5) Make sure you dispose of waste properly, so that it doesn't harm the environment.
6) Put materials away safely so they can't fall or slide and injure anyone.

> COSHH stands for the Control of Substances Hazardous to Health. The COSHH regulations were introduced in 1988 to protect people from the effects of hazardous substances, materials and processes. Employers have to find out what the health hazards of the materials they're using are — and put appropriate control measures in place. For example, protective gear has to be tested regularly and employers must ensure that workers follow the correct safety procedures.

If an Accident Happens, it Needs to be Reported

1) No matter how careful you are, accidents can still sometimes happen. All accidents and injuries need to be recorded, no matter how minor they are.
2) It's important that workshops have a clear accident procedure (a set of instructions) so that people know what to do if there's an accident, and how the accident should be reported.
3) The accident procedure should be clearly displayed and cover things like:

- Where the nearest emergency exits and assembly points are
- Who the first aiders are
- Where the medical room is
- Who the accident should be reported to

1) In a school workshop, you should report all accidents to your teacher straight away. In industry, accidents are recorded on an incident report form and kept in a file.
2) Most companies have a health and safety officer who will investigate each accident to find out what caused it and to see if anything can be done to reduce the risk of the same accident happening again.

Practice Questions

1) What protective equipment should you wear if you are:
   a) working with toxic chemicals?
   b) welding metal?
   c) making a lot of dust while sanding?
   d) casting metal?
2) List four health and safety procedures that should be followed when using tools and machinery.
3) What does COSHH stand for? Why do the COSHH regulations matter?
4) Outline three things that an accident procedure should cover.

Health and Safety

You might have seen lots of <u>symbols</u> dotted around your <u>workshop</u> — here's what they mean...

Symbols are used to Tell People About Safety Risks

1) <u>Signs</u> in workshops give people <u>information</u> about <u>potential risks</u>.

2) The signs need to be understood by people who speak <u>any language</u>, so <u>symbols</u> are often used instead of text (although many signs include written information as well).

3) The symbols come in <u>different shapes</u> and <u>colours</u> depending on what their purpose is.

Yellow triangles — warn you of a potential HAZARD. E.g.

CAUTION
A general warning to take care and be aware of any potential hazards.

HIGH VOLTAGE
Used to show that there's a risk of electric shock from equipment in the area.

Blue circles — tell you something you <u>MUST</u> do. E.g.

EYE PROTECTION MUST BE WORN
Found on machines which could cause objects to <u>fly</u> off towards the user, e.g. <u>lathes</u> or <u>pillar drills</u>.

WEAR FACE MASK
Found on machines that may create <u>harmful dust</u> such as <u>sanding machines</u>.

Red circles — tell you something you <u>MUST NOT</u> do. E.g.

NO ENTRY
Used to stop <u>unauthorised</u> people going into a potentially <u>dangerous</u> area.

NO FOOD OR DRINK
Used to prevent <u>spillages</u> that could cause a <u>slip hazard</u> or <u>contamination</u>.

Green rectangles — give you <u>INFORMATION</u>. E.g.

EMERGENCY EXIT
Often combined with <u>arrows</u> to show the <u>quickest route</u> out of a building in case of fire or other emergency.

EMERGENCY STOP BUTTON
Shows where the <u>emergency stop button</u> is on a piece of machinery.

Orange squares — tell you about <u>DANGEROUS CHEMICALS</u>. E.g.

CORROSIVE SUBSTANCE
Found on bottles containing chemicals that can <u>destroy</u> certain materials on <u>contact</u> and cause <u>burns</u> on skin.

FLAMMABLE SUBSTANCE
Found on bottles containing chemicals that <u>set light</u> easily.

Whenever I see cymbals I always put on ear protection...

This page doesn't cover <u>every single</u> symbol you might see — there are <u>hundreds</u> of 'em. But learn what the <u>shapes</u> and <u>colours</u> mean, then you'll know what <u>kind</u> of information a symbol is giving you.

Health and Safety

Risk Assessments Should be Carried Out

1) A <u>risk assessment</u> is an <u>evaluation</u> carried out by an employer to <u>identify</u> and <u>minimise</u> any potential dangers at work. A risk assessment has to be carried out when any <u>new project</u> is being planned.

2) Risk assessments are especially important when <u>chemicals</u> or <u>machinery</u> are being used.

3) When you're writing a risk assessment think:

> 1) What could be a <u>hazard</u>?
> 2) What <u>precautions</u> could I take to make sure the risk is minimised?

Risk assessment for project

Hazard	How to reduce the risk
Clothing could get caught in the sanding machine.	Tuck clothes in and wear an apron.
Fine dust created when using a sanding machine.	Wear a mask and use a dust extractor.
Fingers could be cut when using a craft knife.	Use a safety rule to protect fingers.

4) Many hazards present an <u>immediate, obvious risk</u>, e.g. working with sharp tools.

5) Others aren't so obvious. For example, using CAD software is usually pretty safe but if you stare at the screen for <u>long periods</u> of time without having a break you could get a <u>headache</u> (and a <u>sore back</u> as well if you sit in an uncomfortable chair).

EXAM TIP
Each hazard and each precaution could be worth one mark. That's <u>a lot</u> of marks altogether.

Practice Questions

1) Why is it important that signs displaying <u>safety symbols</u> are put up in workshops?
2) What do <u>yellow triangles</u> on safety signs tell you?
3) What do <u>blue circles</u> on safety signs tell you?
4) When should you wear a <u>face mask</u> in a workshop?
5) Why is it important not to have <u>food and drink</u> in a workshop?
6) What do <u>corrosive substances</u> do?
7) Dave is planning a project and needs to write a <u>risk assessment</u>.
   a) What is a risk assessment?
   b) The project will involve cutting MDF with a fret saw. Write a risk assessment to cover the possible hazards of this process.

Exam Technique

1) The exam is made up of 1 paper called 'Sustainability and technical aspects of designing and making' — it's 1 hour 30 minutes long and worth 80 marks.

2) The paper will test everything you've learned on the course.

The Paper Has Two Parts...

Section A Contains Mostly Short Answer Questions...

Section A will test you on sustainability, product analysis and design. It will contain 15 short answer questions, including multiple choice and true or false questions, as well as some questions where you have to write a few words. It will also contain one extended answer question (see next page).

---

1 A Fair Trade product is one that:

    (a) can be recycled

    (b) is made in a less economically developed country

    (c) will rot in the environment

    (d) is made by people who are paid fairly   *(1 mark)*

> Read all the answers — don't just go for the first one that sounds possible.

> If you don't know the answer to a multiple choice, you might as well guess. You won't lose a mark, and you might get lucky.

2 State the meaning of the symbol shown below.

The product or packaging is recyclable.
....
                                              (1 mark)

> Remember that you could get asked about anything on the course, so you need to be prepared to answer different styles of questions about a wide range of subjects.

3 What name is given to a design which fits the user well and so won't cause health problems?

Ergonomic design.
....
                                              (1 mark)

> Make sure you've learned all the terms in the glossary.

4 What does 'CAD/CAM' stand for?

Computer Aided Design/Computer Aided Manufacture
....
                                              (1 mark)

Decide whether the statement is **true** or **false**.

Tick to show your answer.

5 Thermosetting plastics can't be recycled.   **True** ☑ **False** ☐

                                              (1 mark)

> Read questions like this really carefully or you could throw marks away. E.g. if you accidentally read this question as "Thermosetting plastics CAN be recycled", you could give the wrong answer even if you understand the subject and know the right answer.

6 Reusing products, like plastic milk crates, uses energy and new materials.   **True** ☐ **False** ☑

                                              (1 mark)

> Don't spend much more than a minute on each of these questions — there's only 1 mark for each.

Exam Technique

...With One Extended Answer Question

The extended answer question in section A could ask for <u>sketching</u>, <u>annotation</u>, <u>short sentences</u> and <u>extended writing</u>. Take a look at this example:

16 A company that manufactures outdoor play equipment has sketched an initial idea for a slide. Fig. 1 shows the slide.

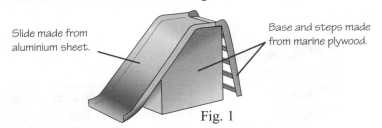

Slide made from aluminium sheet.

Base and steps made from marine plywood.

Fig. 1

a The slide is to be used by children in nursery school playgrounds. Produce an annotated sketch to show how the design could be developed to make it fit for purpose.

(4 marks)

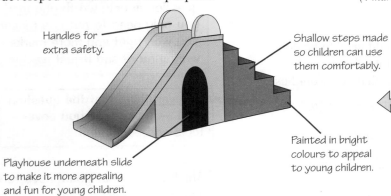

Handles for extra safety.

Shallow steps made so children can use them comfortably.

Playhouse underneath slide to make it more appealing and fun for young children.

Painted in bright colours to appeal to young children.

> Do your drawing in <u>3D</u> (see p. 14-15 for some techniques) **and** <u>render</u> **it (add shading). Use a** <u>ruler</u> **for the** <u>straight lines</u>**.**

b Explain what is meant by the term sustainability.

Sustainability means not causing permanent damage to the

environment and not using up finite resources.

(2 marks)

> The paper is called 'Sustainability and technical aspects of designing and making' — so there's a good chance that there'll be a question about sustainability in your exam.

c *Explain how the slide could be made sustainable.

Recycled materials could be used in its manufacture, meaning that it

would require less energy to produce than if new materials were used.

The coloured parts could be painted using non-toxic paint, which is

less harmful to the environment. It could also be built in a way that

allows it to be dissassembled and individual components removed,

e.g. by ensuring that any screws are accessible. This would mean

that its components could be recycled or reused at the end of its 'life',

and would also make the slide easy to repair with replacement parts.

(6 marks)

> The asterisk (*) means you can get extra marks for <u>good written communication</u> in this question. So check your <u>spelling</u> and use good English. And think about what you want to say <u>before</u> you start writing so you can put your points in a sensible order.

Exam Technique

1) The questions in section B will be about the <u>technical aspects</u> of <u>using equipment</u> and the <u>design</u> of <u>products</u>.

2) It will contain three <u>extended answer questions</u> that could ask for <u>sketching</u>, <u>annotation</u>, <u>short sentences</u> and <u>extended writing</u>.

---

17 Look at this design for a letter holder.

a Suggest a specific suitable material that could be used to make the product.
Give a reason for your answer.

Material _acrylic_

(1 mark)

Reason _It can be bent into shape easily._

(1 mark)

> The question asks for a <u>specific</u> material — so don't just put plastic.

> There's usually more than one reason why a material is suitable — but the question is only worth <u>one mark</u> so you only need to put <u>one reason</u>. You won't get any more marks for writing more and it just <u>wastes time</u>.

b Describe two processes that would need to be done before the letter holder is bent into shape.
Include the tools and equipment that you would use.

1. _Mark out the shape using a try square to draw_
   the right angles and a ruler for the lines.

2. _Clamp the acrylic so it can't slip and cut out_
   the shape using a coping saw.

(4 marks)

> Do <u>everything</u> that the question asks — make sure you cover tools and equipment.

> Think about what you'd have to do <u>before</u> you start cutting — it's a good idea to think about <u>safety procedures</u>. Then, don't forget to name <u>specific tools</u> — a hacksaw would also be suitable here.

c *Discuss why a manufacturer might choose to use CAD/CAM to produce 5000 letter holders.

Using CAD/CAM will mean the products are accurate and
consistent. The shape can be drawn using CAD software
and then copied and pasted so that a CAM machine will
cut out several at once. The shapes can be arranged on
the sheet in the most economical way to reduce waste.
They can be cut out at high speed using a laser cutter.
Because machines are doing the majority of the work,
there's less potential for human error. The high set-up
costs will be recovered by the fast output.

(6 marks)

> This is another '<u>Quality of Written Communication</u>' question — so check your spelling, grammar and punctuation and use the proper <u>technical words</u>.

Exam Technique

18 The top of a greenhouse table is made from strips of aluminium.

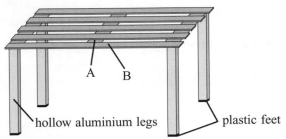

hollow aluminium legs   plastic feet

Question 19: Modify this llama so that it will also hold 20 DVDs.

a Describe how the aluminium strips A and B could be joined together.

The strips could be joined by rivets. A hole must be drilled through both strips to be joined and the rivet inserted with a set. The other end is flattened into another head with a hammer.

(3 marks)

> When you're picking a joining method think about what'll work with the <u>materials</u>, and what'll look <u>neatest</u> on the product — you might not want 15 wing nuts sticking out, say.

> The <u>number of lines</u> you're given for your answer is a big clue to <u>how much</u> you should write (as well as the number of <u>marks</u>).

b The greenhouse table has plastic feet. Describe how the plastic feet could be manufactured using press moulding.

A slug of thermosetting plastic powder is put into a female mould shaped like one of the feet. A former is then pressed onto it at a very high pressure and temperature. This pushes the slug into the mould and liquifies the powder. The powder then sets permanently into the shape of the mould, producing a plastic foot.

(4 marks)

> Make sure your answer fits the question — here you need to describe how <u>plastic feet</u> could be produced by press moulding and not just give a general description of the process.

c The table is to have a shelf beneath it. The height of the shelf should be adjustable. Use sketches and notes to show how the design could be modified to include this.

> You might need to sketch <u>more than one view</u> to show your idea clearly.

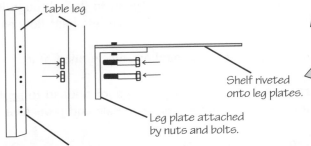

table leg

Shelf riveted onto leg plates.

Leg plate attached by nuts and bolts.

Drill several sets of holes through the legs to allow shelf to be fixed at different heights.

(4 marks)

> Label all the <u>components</u> you've used and show how the parts will be <u>assembled</u>.

> When you think you've <u>finished</u>, go back and <u>read over</u> your answers to check for <u>mistakes</u>. You might even think of something else you could <u>add</u>.

Glossary

Allen key	One of these
alloy	A <u>mixture</u> of two or more metals, or a metal mixed with other elements.
annealing	<u>Softening metal</u> by <u>heating</u> and leaving to <u>cool</u>.
anthropometrics	<u>Body</u> measurement data.
biodegradable	Something that will <u>decay over time</u>, e.g. paper. (Glass, metal and most plastics are <u>not</u> biodegradable.)
brass	A <u>yellowish metal</u> that's an <u>alloy</u> of <u>zinc and copper</u>.
brazing	Joining pieces of metal together using a '<u>filler</u>' metal such as brass spelter. Stronger than soldering but not as strong as welding.
BSI	British Standards Institution. It <u>sets standards</u> for the <u>quality</u> and <u>safety</u> of products and methods. A product that meets these standards can display the <u>Kitemark</u>.
buffing	Polishing a surface to a shine.
CAD/CAM	<u>Designing</u> and <u>manufacturing</u> using a <u>computer</u>.
carbon footprint	The amount of harmful <u>greenhouse gases</u> produced, for example, when manufacturing or using a product.
casting	Making a solid object by pouring a <u>molten material</u> into a <u>mould</u> and waiting for it to cool and set.
ceramics	Brittle materials made by <u>heating clay</u> in an oven.
components	The <u>different parts</u> that are assembled to make a product.
composite	A material made by <u>combining other materials</u>, e.g. glass-reinforced plastic is a composite made from plastic and glass fibres.
conductor	An <u>electrical conductor</u> is a material that allows <u>electricity</u> to <u>flow</u> through it easily, e.g. copper. A <u>thermal conductor</u> is a material that lets <u>heat</u> flow easily.
corrosion	The '<u>eating away</u>' of a material by a chemical reaction, e.g. rusting of iron.
COSHH	Control of Substances Hazardous to Health. <u>Regulations</u> introduced to <u>protect people</u> from the dangers of hazardous substances, materials and processes.
design specification	A list of <u>conditions</u> that a product should meet.
disassembly	Taking a product apart to see how it was <u>made</u>.
ductile	Ductile materials can be <u>drawn into wires</u> easily.

Glossary

enamel	Enamel paint dries to a <u>hard</u>, <u>shiny finish</u>.
ergonomic	<u>Easy</u> and <u>comfortable</u> for people to <u>use</u>.
ferrous	Ferrous metals are ones that contain <u>iron</u>.
finite	A finite resource is one that will <u>run out eventually</u>.
flammable	Something that <u>catches fire easily</u>, e.g. petrol.
flexible	Something that <u>bends</u> a lot <u>without breaking</u>.
globalisation	<u>Buying</u> and <u>selling</u> on a worldwide scale.
hardwood	Hardwood comes from trees with <u>broad leaves</u>, e.g. oak, mahogany. It is usually denser and harder than softwood.
hazard	A potential <u>danger</u> to humans or the environment.
insulator	An <u>electrical insulator</u> is something that <u>does not allow electricity to flow</u> easily, e.g. polythene. A <u>thermal insulator</u> doesn't allow much <u>heat</u> to flow.
knock-down fittings	<u>Non-permanent</u> joints which enable furniture to be assembled and taken apart easily.
laminated	<u>Covered</u> with a layer of <u>another material</u>.
landfill	A landfill site is a large <u>rubbish dump</u> that's eventually covered with earth.
linear	Linear motion is when something moves in a <u>straight line</u> in <u>one direction</u>.
malleable	Malleable materials are easy to <u>shape and bend</u>, e.g. thin metal sheets.
market pull	When a product is made due to <u>consumer demand</u>.
model	A <u>practice version</u> of a product that you make during the development stage. It's probably made from easy-to-work materials and might be scaled down in size.
nanotechnology	Working with materials on a <u>really small scale</u>.
non-ferrous	Non-ferrous metals are ones that <u>don't contain iron</u>.
prototype	A full-size, working, one-off model of a design. A prototype is built to allow <u>evaluation</u> of the product before starting manufacturing in quantity.
quality assurance	The <u>system</u> that is set up to make sure that <u>high quality</u> products are produced.
quality control	The <u>checks</u> that are carried out on materials and products throughout production to make sure that standards are being met.
refinery	A <u>chemical plant</u> where chemicals are processed, e.g. an oil refinery.

Glossary

renewable	A renewable resource is one that is <u>replaced</u> by natural processes as fast as it is <u>consumed</u> by humans, e.g. softwood trees in a plantation.
risk assessment	Identifying potential <u>hazards</u> and the <u>precautions</u> needed to minimise dangers before work starts.
scribing	<u>Scoring a line</u> onto a surface (usually before cutting or folding).
smart material	A material that <u>changes its properties</u> in response to a change in its environment.
softwood	Softwood comes from trees with <u>needle-like leaves</u>, e.g. pine, cedar. It's usually <u>less dense</u> and easier to saw than hardwood.
soldering	Joining two metals together by melting a tin-based alloy between them. Not as strong as brazing or welding.
spelter	An alloy of zinc.
sustainable	A sustainable process or material is one that can be used without causing <u>permanent damage</u> to the environment or using up finite resources, e.g. sustainable wood comes from forests where fast-growing trees are chopped down and replaced.
synthetic	Man-made.
target market	The group of people who you want to <u>sell</u> your product to.
tarnishing	When a metal surface <u>loses its shine</u> and becomes dull. Tarnishing happens because of reactions with the air.
technology push	When advances in technology drive the design of <u>new</u> products and the <u>re-design</u> of old products.
thermoplastics	Plastics that can be <u>melted and remoulded</u> over and over again.
thermosetting	Thermosetting plastics are ones that undergo a <u>chemical change</u> when heated which makes them hard and rigid. They can't be remoulded.
tolerance	How much a component can <u>differ</u> in size from its <u>ideal measurements</u> before the product is affected.
toxic	A toxic substance is one that's <u>harmful to health</u>.
veneer	A <u>thin layer</u> of high quality <u>wood</u>.
warped	When something has <u>changed shape</u>, e.g. untreated wood warps after time.
welding	Joining two metals together using very high temperatures to melt the edges of a joint so that they flow together.
working drawing	A detailed scale drawing that shows all the dimensions of each part of a product, the materials from which components are to be made, etc.

Answers

Page 3 — Design Issues

1) a) Market pull is the effect of consumer demand on the design of a product.
    b) e.g. laptop computers
2) Most plastic products are made from oil so manufacturers will have to find alternative resources.
3) a) Materials can be sourced from where they are cheapest and then processed in countries where energy and wages are cheap.
    b) Selling products worldwide means that designers have to take factors like culture, language and power sources into account.
4) New technology might allow Arthur's MP3 player to be cheaper to produce, hold more songs, have better sound quality or additional features (e.g. touch screen technology) than older MP3 players.
5) Production costs could be reduced, as materials could be sourced from where they're cheapest and manufacturing could be done where wages and energy are cheapest. The sheds could be sold worldwide, making more money.

Page 5 — Product Analysis and Market Research

1) a) E.g. what kind of product is needed, how the product will be used, who the product is for.
    b) the client
2) How well the product can do the function it's intended for.
3) How the product was made and how it works.
4) a) young children (or their parents)
    b) plastic and metal
5) To find out what people like or dislike about similar existing products and to check whether or not people will want to buy your product.

Page 7 — Design Specification and Proposals

1) a) A list of conditions that the product must meet.
    b) e.g. colour / material / production method / size / weight / price range
    c) E.g. must hold two eggs and four slices of toast, should have a shiny surface finish, must be easy to clean, no more than 10 cm tall, must cost less than £2 to manufacture.
2) a) e.g. a flower, a leaf, a bird's nest
    b) & c) Any suitable sketches that meet the specification.

Page 9 — Development

1) a) Ergonomics is about how easy and comfortable a product is to use.
    b) Anthropometrics need to be considered, e.g. the average size of people's hands. Its size and proportions need to fit the user and their needs, e.g. keys not too small and the keyboard should sit low on the desk. (Or similar answer.)
    c) They could experience health problems, e.g. hand / wrist strain, backache.
2) a) body measurement data
    b) the handle
    c) Its size and shape.
3) a) E.g. the material needs to be strong enough to support the weight of items that will be put on it / it needs to be lightweight and portable / it must be able to withstand outdoor conditions.
    b) It should appeal to campers.
    c) The materials need to be suitable for the price of the product, so if it's going to be sold cheaply then the materials also need to be cheap.

Page 11 — Modelling

1) E.g. it will help her to decide on the finer details of her design, such as the sizes or positions of components and how they should be assembled.
2) E.g. you can spot and solve problems / you can try out different components/construction methods / you can try reducing the number of parts to make construction easier.
3) E.g. cardboard, foam board, corrugated plastic (corriflute), MDF, plasticard, STYROFOAM™
4) It can be used to model designs in 3D.
5) To check the product is exactly right, works properly and is safe. Consumers might test the prototype — if it gets good feedback, the product might go into commercial production.

Page 13 — Planning

1) E.g. construction details / tools and equipment / materials / sizes / quality control instructions / time schedules / health and safety information.
2) To help limit the number of problems that occur.
3) Put the quality control checks in diamond shaped boxes.
4) a) Some of the processes can happen at the same time, e.g. while the varnish is drying.
    b) 75 minutes
    c) Making the table legs — it takes 25 minutes.

Page 15 — Drawing Techniques

1) Vanishing points are the points where lines going into the distance are drawn to.
2)

3) Advantage — it's easier to get dimensions right. Disadvantage — it doesn't show things smaller the further away they are.

4)

5) a) Centre lines (alternate short/long dashes) and hidden details (short dashes)
    b) millimetres

Page 17 — Properties of Materials

1) a) The material will stretch and return to its original shape.
    b) The material can be moulded.
    c) The material can be drawn into wires.
2) a) e.g. an extension lead
    b) e.g. a file / drill
    c) e.g. armour / bulletproof vest
3) E.g. bridge supports — need to resist squashing forces.
    E.g. rope in a tug of war — need to resist pulling forces.
4) a) E.g. modern appearance and opaque.
    b) The material she chooses must be suitable for the manufacturing method she's planning to use.

Answers

Page 19 — Woods and Boards

1) a) e.g. pine / cedar / yew
   b) e.g. oak / mahogany / beech / elm

2) They take longer to grow.

3) a)

Veneers
Strips of softwood

   b) Two from, e.g: chipboard / MDF / plywood
   c) chipboard — cheap self-assembly furniture,
       MDF — kitchen cabinets,
       plywood — building and furniture
   d) They contain glue.

4) More trees can be replanted to replace those cut down.

5) It can be shredded to make things like compost, playground flooring or chipboard. Good quality wood, e.g. undamaged floorboards, can be cleaned up and reused to make furniture.

Page 21 — Wood Finishes

1) Staining allows the grain of the wood to show through.

2) a) He should sand and then prime the toy chest.
   b) Undercoat and polyurethane.

3) a) polyurethane varnish
   b) Apply sanding sealer.

4) a) Oil gives more protection, and is quicker to apply.
   b) He could stain it with an 'oak' stain.

Page 23 — Metals

1) A metal that contains iron.

2) Two from, e.g. mild steel is cheaper than high-carbon steel, which is cheaper than stainless steel.

3) Two from, e.g. aluminium is cheaper than brass, which is cheaper than copper.

4) It's made from a mixture of iron and carbon.

5) e.g. brass

6) Five from, e.g. sheet, strip, bars, pipe, angle, U-shaped channel, I-shaped girder.

7) Yes — copper is a good conductor of electricity and is ductile.

8) High-carbon steel — it's hard so won't dent when it is used.

9) It doesn't rust / corrode.

10) a) Aluminium — it's lightweight and corrosion-resistant.
    b) E.g. cost, the shapes and sizes it's available in.

Page 25 — Metals

1) It needs to be smoothed, e.g. filed, and degreased.

2) a) To protect it from corrosion / the weather.
   b) plastic coating — electrical wires
       polishing — chrome bodywork on cars/bikes
       lacquering — jewellery

3) Metal ores contain the metal along with other substances.

4) The metal is separated from the other substances in the ore (often in a blast furnace). Molten metal is poured into a casting machine where it's cooled and run through rollers to make blocks.

5) Metals usually still have some impurities after they've been processed. Some products need very pure metal, so the impurities have to be removed.

6) Digging up the metal ore damages the landscape.
   The processing and refining plants produce air/water pollution.
   Transporting the metal also produces air and noise pollution.

7) It reduces the amount of metal ore that needs to be extracted from the ground. This helps to conserve metal ore, which is a finite resource. It also saves energy.

Page 27 — Plastics

1) a) e.g. acrylic / ABS / polystyrene / polythene / nylon / PVC / polypropylene
   b) e.g. epoxy resin / urea-formaldehyde / melamine-formaldehyde / polyester resin

2) E.g. urea-formaldehyde — it will not melt when the pan gets hot.

3) Five from, e.g. powder, granules, pellets, liquid, film, sheets, rods, tubes.

4) a) It's durable / resistant to corrosion.
   b) Using wet and dry paper or a buffing machine.

5) Crude oil is extracted from the ground. The oil is taken to a refinery where it's processed into different substances. Some of these are then processed further to make plastics.

6) When they're heated they undergo a chemical change and become hard and rigid. Once you've heated and moulded them once they can't be melted and reshaped again.

7) Two from, e.g. crude oil used to make plastics is a finite resource, and we are using it up very quickly. / They take hundreds of years to degrade if they're disposed of in landfill. / Turning crude oil into plastic produces a lot of pollution/uses a lot of energy.

Page 29 — Changing Properties

1) A material made from two or more materials bonded together.

2) a) It's much stronger.
   b) It's cheaper.
   c) Any two from, e.g. in protective helmets / racing cars / laptops / sports equipment / bulletproof vests.
   d) e.g. in car bodies and boats

3) a) It's resistant to abrasion.
   b) It adds a lot of strength without adding much weight.

4) Annealing involves heating a metal and leaving it to cool slowly. Hardening involves heating it and then cooling it rapidly. Annealing makes metals softer, more ductile and less brittle. Hardening makes metals harder but brittle.

5) a) tempering
   b) The metal needs to be cleaned and then heated. As it gets hotter it will change colour — the colour shows how tough the metal's become.

Page 31 — Smart and Modern Materials

1) a) A material that reacts to changes in the environment.
   b) It returns to a remembered shape when it's heated.
   c) e.g. to make glasses frames
   d) e.g. thermochromic pigments / thermochromic sheets / polymorph / hydromorph plastics

2) a) Alu composite sheet
   b) Flexiply®

3) If there's a cheaper or more sustainable alternative.

Page 33 — Nanotechnology

1) Really tiny lumps of material.

2) He might have added an antibacterial coating.

3) a) water-repellent coating
   b) self cleaning glass

4) e.g. bike frames / tennis racquet frames

Answers

5) Nanoparticles are very small and lightweight so could be carried into the atmosphere or contaminate water sources. / The technology is too new for us to know if there are any long-term risks to using nanoparticles.

Page 35 — Fixtures and Fittings

1) screws / nuts and bolts
2) nuts and bolts
3) Because they're quick to use.
4) leg plates
5) dowels

Page 37 — Fixtures and Fittings

1) flush hinge
2) a) butt hinge
   b) tee hinge
3) You can lift the door off the hinge.
4) E.g. steel / brass — the material needs to be strong.
5) They hold a door closed without locking.
6) Draws will slide smoothly and won't pull out.
7) screws

Page 39 — Preparing and Measuring Materials

1) To measure the thickness or diameter of materials.
2) So that you know exactly where to cut them.
3) E.g. marking knife — to mark the wood and cut the wood fibres to stop it splitting when it's sawn / sliding bevel — to guide the marking knife along the correct angle.
4) Keep the marks as thin as possible. Always cut on the waste side of the line so that the material doesn't end up too small.
5) a) He can make holes in the wood to start off drilling or to help put in screws.
   b) He is using wood — centre punches are for use on metal or plastic.

Page 41 — Hand Tools

1) hacksaw
2) Cutting curves in wood and plastic.
3) bench plane / surform
4) Twist bit — for drilling small holes. Flat bit — for drilling large flat-bottomed holes.
5) a) a gouger
   b) a cold chisel

Page 43 — Power and Machine Tools

1) Any two from, e.g. do a visual check for any loose connections before you start / run your hand along the lead to check for any cuts in the insulation / check that the blade or drill bit is attached correctly and tightly / use an RCD to help prevent electric shocks / wear a mask or fit an extraction hose / wear safety glasses / make sure clothing can't get caught / clamp your work so it can't slip or move / make sure you know where the stop buttons are before you start.
2) a) planer
   b) router
3) a jigsaw
4) To remove material to produce the required size or shape.
   To remove material to make a surface absolutely flat.

5) a) E.g. check that all the guards are in place and aren't cracked.
   b) It should be held straight and tightly secured at both ends to stop it wobbling.

Page 45 — Forming and Bending

1) sheet metal folder
2) a) heat it
   b)
3) (Hot) metals are placed on it to be hammered into shape.
4) a) The strips of wood are glued together and held in a jig, which keeps them bent in the desired shape while the glue dries.
   b) E.g. rocking chair runners, chair/table legs.
5) a) line bending
   b) The element in the line bender heats the plastic along the line where you want to bend it. Once the plastic is soft, it can be bent.

Page 47 — Casting and Moulding

1) a) thermosetting plastics
   b) A 'slug' of thermosetting plastic powder is put into a 'female' mould. A former is pressed onto it and pushes the plastic into the mould. Very high temperatures and pressures liquify the powder. The plastic sets permanently into the shape of the mould.
2) A sheet of thermoplastic is heated until it goes soft. A mould is put onto the vacuum bed. The bed is then lifted close to the heated plastic. The air is sucked out from under the plastic. This forces the plastic onto the mould.
3) a) blow moulding
   b)
4) a) a mould
   b) metal and thermoplastics
5) a) a plastic
   b) Molten plastic is forced into a closed mould under pressure.
6) e.g. plastic covered wire, plastic/aluminium edgings

Page 49 — Fabricating

1) a) woodscrews
   b) Three from, e.g. round / countersunk / slotted / cross.
2) a) Temporary fittings which enable furniture to be assembled and taken apart easily.
   b) Advantage — e.g. they're fast to use / they can be taken apart easily.
      Disadvantage — e.g. they aren't as strong as glued joints.
   c) (cheap) flat-pack furniture
3) Advantage — e.g. the joints that screws make are stronger / the joints can be taken apart so the product can be disassembled.
   Disadvantage — they're slower to use than nails are.

Page 51 — Fabricating

1) They aren't very strong.
2) mortise and tenon joint / dowel joint
3) a) acrylic cement/epoxy resin
   b) They're too smooth / they have a greasy texture which stops the glue from keying in.

Answers

Page 53 — Controlling Accuracy

1) Marking out the same shape many times, and checking the accuracy of components when they've been cut.

2) a) E.g. gets rid of the need for complex marking out / helps cut down on errors / makes sure that components are consistent / enables complex joints to be machined quickly and easily.
   b) Because it would take him a long time to make the jig.

3) a) a fence
   b) The fence will be attached to the router, and run along the edge of the wood, keeping the router the same distance away from the edge at all times.
   c) He can set it up to repeat the same action over and over again — so he'll get identical components.

4) a) a mitre fence
   b) She would set the pivot on the mitre fence to 55°. The gauge would then guide the tool towards the material at this angle.

Page 55 — Computerised Production

1) a) Computer Aided Design
   b) e.g. Pro/DESKTOP® or SolidWorks®
   c) E.g. you can model and change your design quickly / it's easy to experiment with alternative colours and forms / you can spot any problems before you make your product.

2) a) Computer Aided Manufacture
   b) The machines follow the x,y,z coordinates from the CAD software, and move the tools to shape the material.

3) E.g. 3D printers can be used to make one-off prototypes.

4) E.g. complicated products can be mass-produced quickly as different parts can be manufactured by different machines and then assembled quickly / lots of products can be manufactured in a short time / CAM machines are really accurate — so large numbers of identical products can be made.

5) e.g. Microsoft® Excel / Microsoft® Access

Page 57 — Social Responsibility

1) a) the BSI Kitemark
   b) The product meets EU safety standards.
   c) The timber has come from a sustainably managed forest.

2) E.g. care instructions and instructions for product disposal.

3) It could give a visible warning signal, e.g. flashing lights.

4) a) E.g. it could have a large, easy-to-grip handle and lever.
   b) Infirm people might have difficulty holding and using a normal tin opener so a larger handle with grips would make it easier for them to use.

Page 59 — Legal and Moral Issues

1) E.g. a sharp knife — if you made it blunter, it wouldn't do its job.

2) Two from, e.g. make sure they don't have sharp corners / make sure the paint or varnish isn't toxic / make sure components are firmly attached.

3) They've already been rigorously tested by their manufacturer.

4) a) The Sale of Goods Act
   b) Fire Safety Regulations

5) Consumers tend to be more willing to buy approved products, or will pay more for them, so having symbols like the BSI Kitemark can make products more profitable.

6) John's employees could go on strike or decide to quit, which would mean his products wouldn't get made. Potential customers might also be put off buying his products, so he could lose money in the long run.

Page 61 — Cultural Issues

1) Three from, e.g. religion / beliefs / laws / language / dress / art / food / traditions.

2) So that you don't offend or exclude people who might want to buy your product.

3) E.g. make sure the table is big enough to seat a typical large family.

4) E.g. a product with a rude slogan or picture — people may think this isn't appropriate if there are young children around.

5) a) E.g. a Union Jack design.
   b) E.g. he might want to avoid any risk of offending people with strong Christian beliefs.

6) E.g. red might appeal to people with a Chinese background because it's associated with good luck.

Page 63 — Sustainability

1) a) A resource that can be replaced.
   b) A resource that will eventually run out.

2) E.g. a simple design, easily accessible parts (wheels, say) that can be replaced.

3) Three from, e.g. paper / card / glass / aluminium / steel / some plastics.

4) Recycling involves reprocessing materials so they can be used again. Reusing means using the product again, either for the same or a different purpose.

5) a) Designing products so that they need replacing after a short amount of time.
   b) Because disposing of old products causes problems like filling up landfill sites and pollution. Also, more materials and energy have to be used to make replacement products.

6) E.g. recycle — he could use a plastic that is recyclable or recycled, reduce — he could keep packaging to a minimum, rethink — he could design a 'two in one' knife and spoon, etc.

Page 65 — Sustainability

1) E.g. disposable razors, mobile phones (there are lots of possible answers to this question).

2) Products are designed so that once they reach the end of their life they can be easily taken apart and the pieces reused or recycled.

3) a) A life cycle analysis looks at each stage in the life of a product and works out the environmental impact.
   b) Choice of material, manufacture, using the product and product disposal.

4) a) E.g. wood is a renewable resource whereas metal is not.
   b) Softwoods tend to be from managed plantations where trees get replanted and regrow quickly. Hardwoods tend to come from natural rainforests, where felling the trees destroys habitats and upsets ecosystems.

5) Any two from, e.g. whether the product contains harmful chemicals / how the product can be recycled / how packaging can be minimised.

Page 67 — Environmental Issues

1) a) The amount of greenhouse gases released by doing or making something.
   b) Carbon dioxide is released when they're made, transported and used. This is because fossil fuels are burned to provide the energy for these processes.
   c) E.g. by making a product more energy-efficient.

Answers

2) Companies are given carbon credits which allow them to emit a certain amount of carbon dioxide. Companies are then allowed to trade these credits with each other.

3) By donating money to a project that reduces carbon emissions. The money should be enough to balance out the greenhouse gases that the company is responsible for.

4) CFCs break down the ozone layer which protects us from the Sun's harmful UV radiation.

5) VOCs are major air pollutants and greenhouse gases. By using paint which doesn't contain them, Sarah is helping the environment.

Page 69 — Production Methods

1) Jobbing production, batch production, mass production, continuous production.

2) Labour costs are high because jobbing production is labour-intensive, and the workforce needs to be highly skilled.

3) a) Batch production.
   b) So they can switch from making a batch of one product to making a batch of another product quickly.

4) Down time is the time between batches when machines are being changed or set up differently. It reduces efficiency because you're not making anything that can be sold.

5) a) Mass production.
   b) It's easy to recruit people because they don't have to be highly skilled.

6) The production is broken down into lots of simple tasks that follow each other on the assembly line. Fred will only have to do the spray painting, because other workers will have the skills for other parts of the process.

7) a) It's highly automated and large quantities can be made very quickly. Production never stops so time is not wasted.
   b) It's only useful for making products that are in constant high demand. The machinery is very expensive so can't be afforded by small companies.

Page 71 — Quality Control

1) Testing samples of components to check that they match the specification.

2) ±3 mm

3) a) and c) would be acceptable, b) and d) wouldn't.

4) They allow dimensions to be checked much more quickly.

5) a) A visual inspection.
   b) To check for defects, e.g. cracks at joints.
   c) E.g. he could load weights onto the table and record when it collapses.
   d) He could use the results to write safety instructions for the table, saying how much weight it will bear.

Page 73 — New Technologies

1) a) An additive process adds material to build up the product. A subtractive process removes material from a larger piece to create a product.
   b) Two from, e.g. CNC routers / lathes / milling machines / laser cutting machines
   c) Two from, e.g. 3D printing / laminating / stereolithography / laser-sintering

2) a) Converting a CAD drawing to a 3D model, usually using 3D printing.
   b) Making components or products using an additive process, e.g. stereolithography, instead of a more traditional method, e.g. moulding.

3) Three from, e.g. products can be machined at high speed so large numbers of product can be made in a short space of time / machines can work in conditions that would be hazardous to people / labour costs are lower because machines are doing most of the work / CAM gives a high quality finish / there's far less potential for human error.

4) One from, e.g. computers can be affected by software problems that might slow down production / fewer workers are needed so unemployment might increase.

5) Two from, e,g, improvements in communication technology / development of CAD/CAM / faster transport.

6) Saving on shipping costs, by sending designs to be manufactured near where they're sold, and saving on labour costs, by making things where labour is cheaper.

Page 75 — Health and Safety

1) a) face mask/goggles, gloves, (breathing apparatus)
   b) gloves, apron and face shield
   c) goggles, face mask, gloves
   d) all-body suit, face shield, gauntlets, spats

2) Any four from: Never leave any machines unattended while switched on. / Know how to switch off and isolate machines in an emergency. / Ensure that any dust extraction equipment is working properly. / Never adjust a machine until you've switched it off and isolated it from the mains first. / Make sure nobody will distract you or knock you when you're working on the machine.

3) Control of Substances Hazardous to Health. They protect people from the dangers of using hazardous materials and processes.

4) Three from, e.g. where the emergency exits are / who the first aiders are / where the medical room is / who the accident should be reported to.

Page 77 — Health and Safety

1) To give people information about potential risks.

2) They warn you of a potential hazard.

3) They tell you something you must do.

4) When using machines that might create harmful dust, e.g. a sanding machine.

5) It could cause a cause a spill, which might lead to a slip hazard, or contamination.

6) They destroy certain materials on contact and cause burns on skin.

7) a) An evaluation carried out to identify and minimise any potential dangers at work.
   b) cuttings fly off — wear goggles,
   work falls off — secure work safely,
   sharp blade — keep fingers away from blade,
   dust inhalation — wear a face mask/provide adequate ventilation/dust extraction,
   clothing catches — wear apron/roll up sleeves,
   someone knocks you — make sure you're the only person working in the area.

Index

Index

Index